THE BANDS

GUITAR
T
A
B
EDITION

GW00646239

WISE PUBLICATIONS
LONDON/NEW YORK/PARIS/SYDNEY/COPENHAGEN/BERLIN/MADRID/TOKYO

EXCLUSIVE DISTRIBUTORS:
MUSIC SALES LIMITED
8/9 FRITH STREET, LONDON W1D 3JB, ENGLAND.
MUSIC SALES PTY LIMITED
120 ROTHSCHILD AVENUE, ROSEBERY, NSW 2018, AUSTRALIA.

ORDER NO. AM976129
ISBN 0-7119-9777-2
THIS BOOK © COPYRIGHT 2002 BY WISE PUBLICATIONS.

PRINTED IN THE UNITED KINGDOM BY
PRINTWISE (HAVERHILL) LIMITED, SUFFOLK.

WWW.MUSICSALES.COM

YOUR GUARANTEE OF QUALITY:

AS PUBLISHERS, WE STRIVE TO PRODUCE EVERY BOOK
TO THE HIGHEST COMMERCIAL STANDARDS.

PARTICULAR CARE HAS BEEN GIVEN TO SPECIFYING
ACID-FREE, NEUTRAL-SIZED PAPER MADE FROM PULPS WHICH
HAVE NOT BEEN ELEMENTAL CHLORINE BLEACHED.

THIS PULP IS FROM FARMED SUSTAINABLE FORESTS AND
WAS PRODUCED WITH SPECIAL REGARD FOR THE ENVIRONMENT.

THROUGHOUT, THE PRINTING AND BINDING HAVE BEEN
PLANNED TO ENSURE A STURDY, ATTRACTIVE PUBLICATION
WHICH SHOULD GIVE YEARS OF ENJOYMENT.

IF YOUR COPY FAILS TO MEET OUR HIGH STANDARDS,
PLEASE INFORM US AND WE WILL GLADLY REPLACE IT.

guitar tablature explained

Guitar music can be notated three different ways: on a musical stave, in tablature, and in rhythm slashes

RHYTHM SLASHES are written above the stave. Strum chords in the rhythm indicated. Round noteheads indicate single notes.

THE MUSICAL STAVE shows pitches and rhythms and is divided by lines into bars. Pitches are named after the first seven letters of the alphabet.

TABLATURE graphically represents the guitar fingerboard. Each horizontal line represents a string, and each number represents a fret.

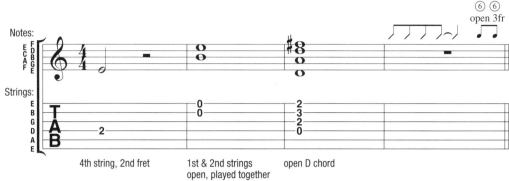

4th string, 2nd fret   1st & 2nd strings open, played together   open D chord

definitions for special guitar notation

SEMI-TONE BEND: Strike the note and bend up a semi-tone (1/2 step).

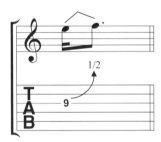

WHOLE-TONE BEND: Strike the note and bend up a whole-tone (whole step).

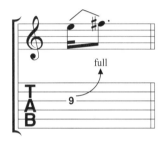

GRACE NOTE BEND: Strike the note and bend as indicated. Play the first note as quickly as possible.

QUARTER-TONE BEND: Strike the note and bend up a 1/4 step.

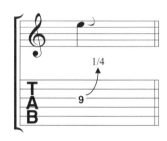

BEND & RELEASE: Strike the note and bend up as indicated, then release back to the original note.

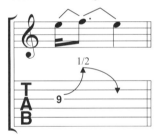

COMPOUND BEND & RELEASE: Strike the note and bend up and down in the rhythm indicated.

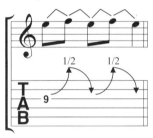

PRE-BEND: Bend the note as indicated, then strike it.

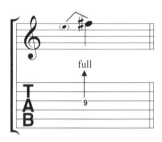

PRE-BEND & RELEASE: Bend the note as indicated. Strike it and release the note back to the original pitch.

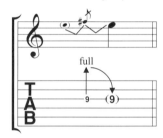

UNISON BEND: Strike the two notes simultaneously and bend the lower note up to the pitch of the higher.

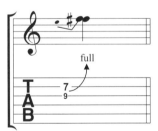

BEND & RESTRIKE: Strike the note and bend as indicated then restrike the string where the symbol occurs.

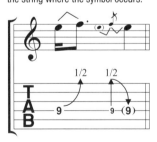

BEND, HOLD AND RELEASE: Same as bend and release but hold the bend for the duration of the tie.

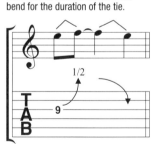

BEND AND TAP: Bend the note as indicated and tap the higher fret while still holding the bend.

VIBRATO: The string is vibrated by rapidly bending and releasing the note with the fretting hand.

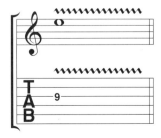

HAMMER-ON: Strike the first note with one finger, then sound the second note (on the same string) with another finger by fretting it without picking.

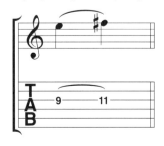

PULL-OFF: Place both fingers on the notes to be sounded, strike the first note and without picking, pull the finger off to sound the second note.

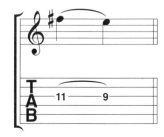

LEGATO SLIDE (GLISS): Strike the first note and then slide the same fret-hand finger up or down to the second note. The second note is not struck.

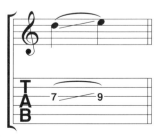

NOTE: The speed of any bend is indicated by the music notation and tempo.

SHIFT SLIDE (GLISS & RESTRIKE): Same as legato slide, except the second note is struck.

TRILL: Very rapidly alternate between the notes indicated by continuously hammering on and pulling off.

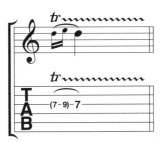

TAPPING: Hammer ("tap") the fret indicated with the pick-hand index or middle finger and pull off to the note fretted by the fret hand.

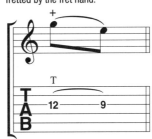

PICK SCRAPE: The edge of the pick is rubbed down (or up) the string, producing a scratchy sound.

MUFFLED STRINGS: A percussive sound is produced by laying the fret hand across the string(s) without depressing, and striking them with the pick hand.

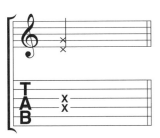

NATURAL HARMONIC: Strike the note while the fret-hand lightly touches the string directly over the fret indicated.

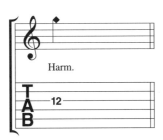

PINCH HARMONIC: The note is fretted normally and a harmonic is produced by adding the edge of the thumb or the tip of the index finger of the pick hand to the normal pick attack.

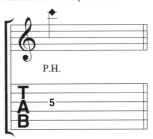

HARP HARMONIC: The note is fretted normally and a harmonic is produced by gently resting the pick hand's index finger directly above the indicated fret (in brackets) while plucking the appropriate string.

PALM MUTING: The note is partially muted by the pick hand lightly touching the string(s) just before the bridge.

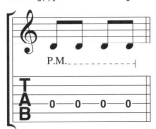

RAKE: Drag the pick across the strings indicated with a single motion.

TREMOLO PICKING: The note is picked as rapidly and continuously as possible.

ARPEGGIATE: Play the notes of the chord indicated by quickly rolling them from bottom to top.

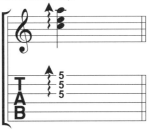

SWEEP PICKING: Rhythmic downstroke and/or upstroke motion across the strings.

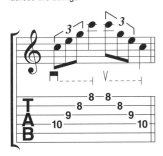

VIBRATO DIVE BAR AND RETURN: The pitch of the note or chord is dropped a specific number of steps (in rhythm) then returned to the original pitch.

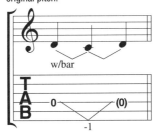

VIBRATO BAR SCOOP: Depress the bar just before striking the note, then quickly release the bar.

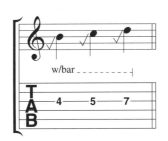

VIBRATO BAR DIP: Strike the note and then immediately drop a specific number of steps, then release back to the original pitch.

additional musical definitions

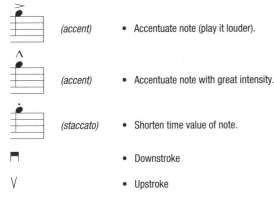

(accent)	•	Accentuate note (play it louder).
(accent)	•	Accentuate note with great intensity.
(staccato)	•	Shorten time value of note.
	•	Downstroke
	•	Upstroke

D.%. al Coda

D.C. al Fine

tacet

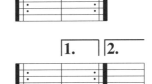

• Go back to the sign (%), then play until the bar marked *To Coda* ⊕ then skip to the section marked ⊕ *Coda*.

• Go back to the beginning of the song and play until the bar marked *Fine*.

• Instrument is silent (drops out).

• Repeat bars between signs.

• When a repeated section has different endings, play the first ending only the first time and the second ending only the second time.

NOTE: Tablature numbers in brackets mean:
1. The note is sustained, but a new articulation (such as hammer on or slide) begins.
2. A note may be fretted but not necessarily played.

BOHEMIAN LIKE YOU

Words & Music by Courtney Taylor-Taylor

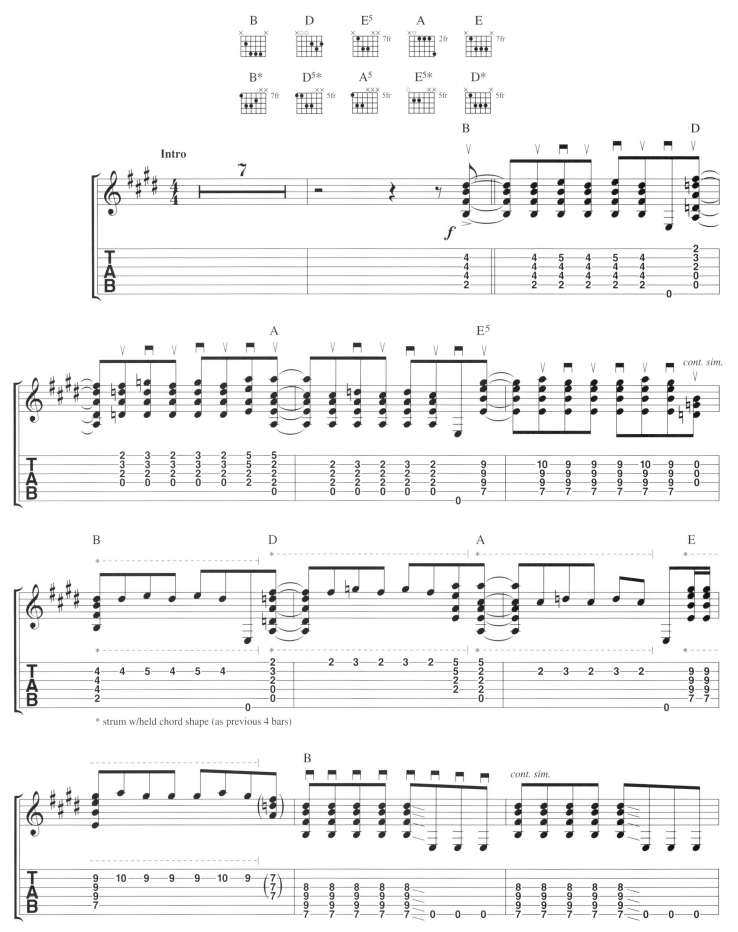

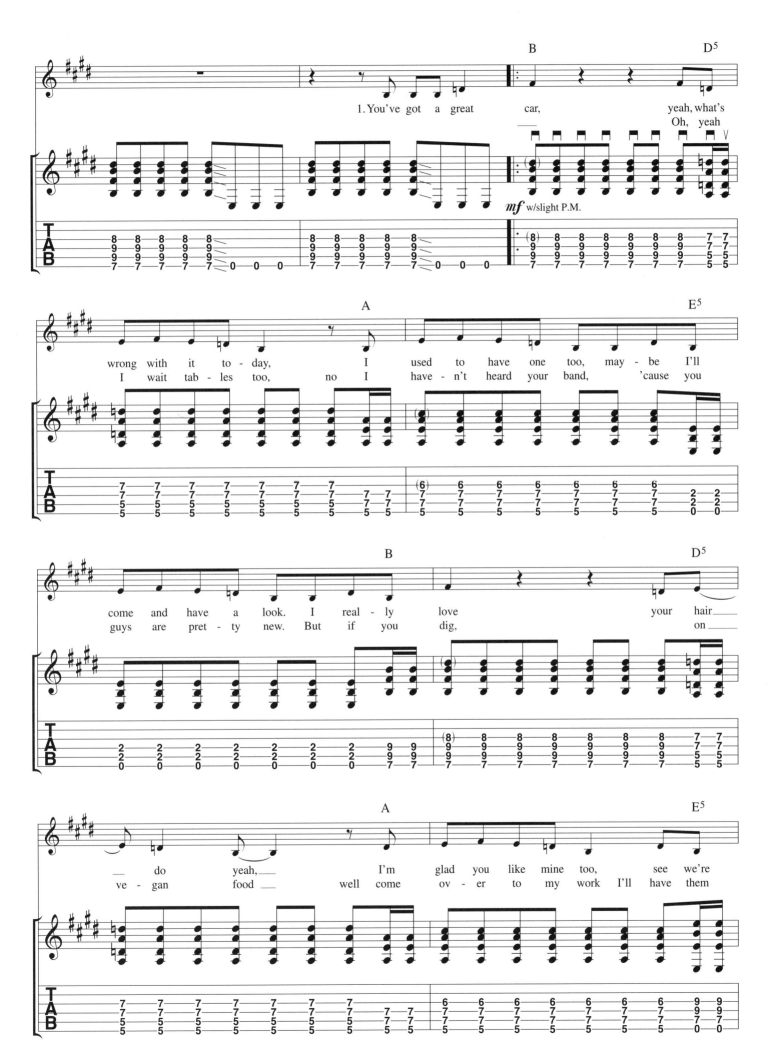

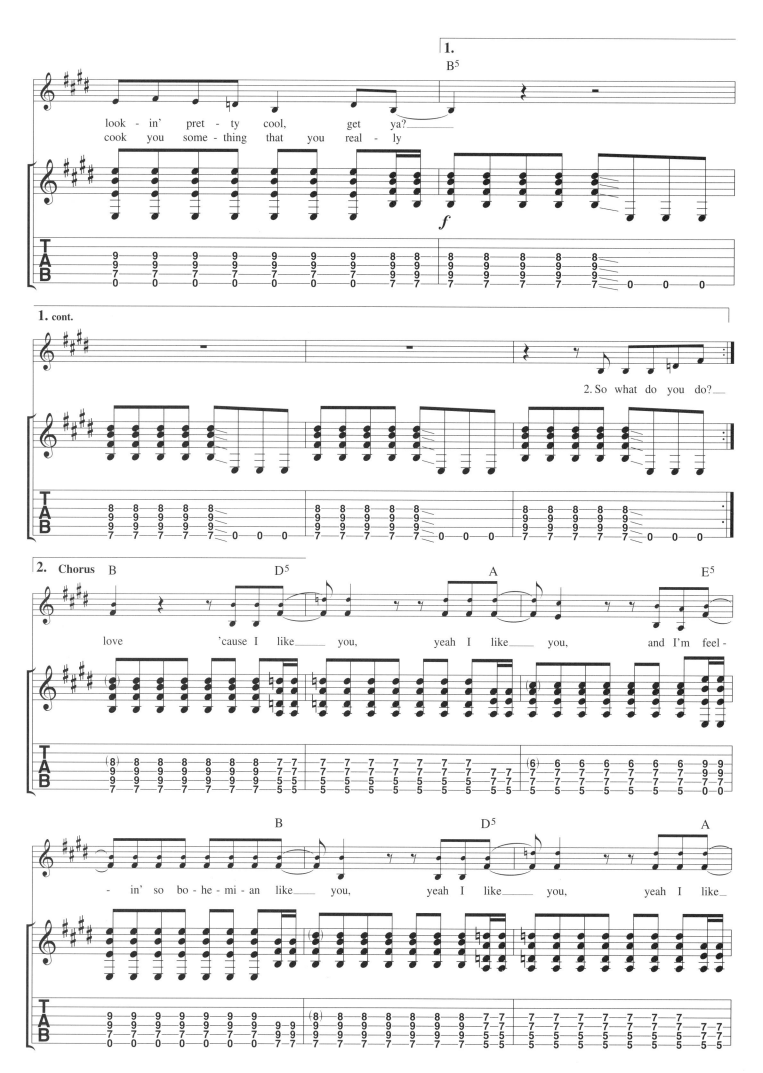

* strum w/held chord shape as previously

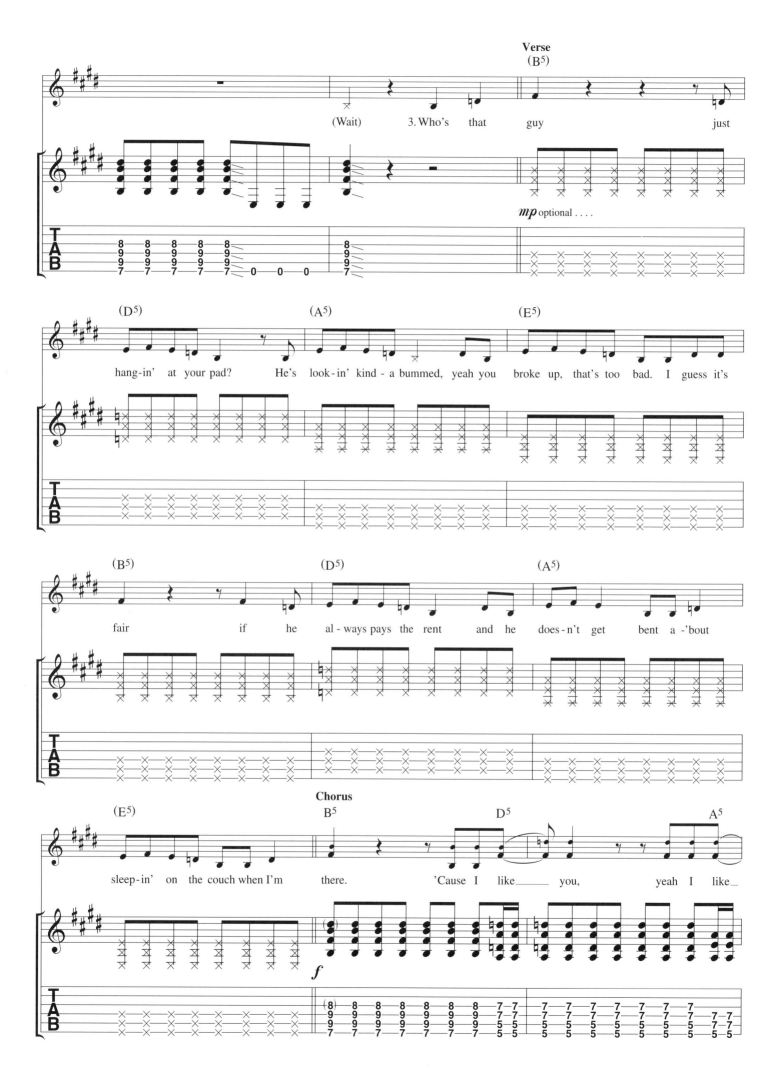

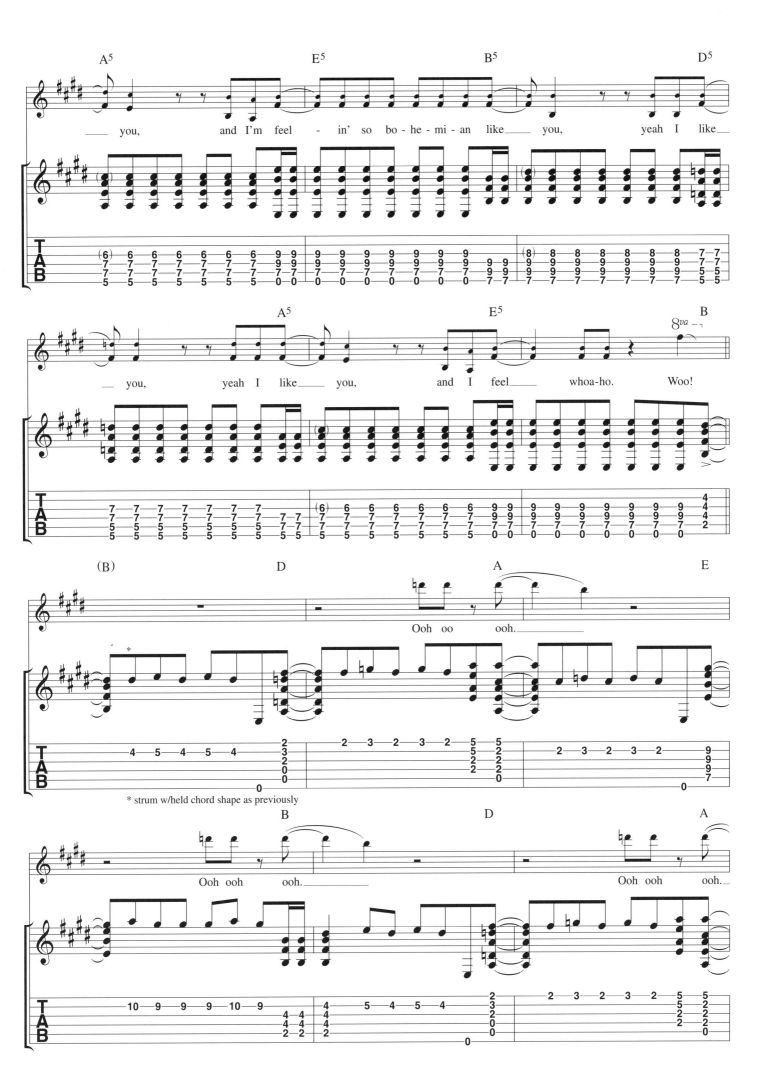

FAT LIP

Words & Music by Greig Nori, Deryck Whibley, Steve Jocz & Dave Baksh

Tune 6th string to D

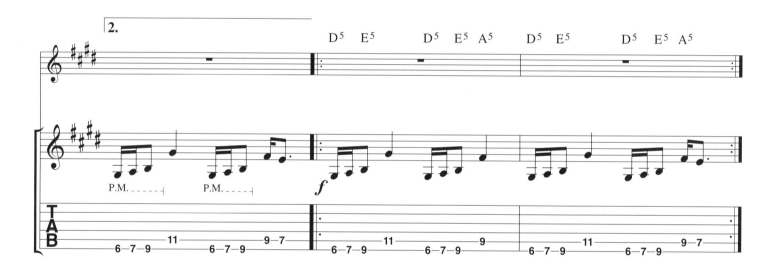

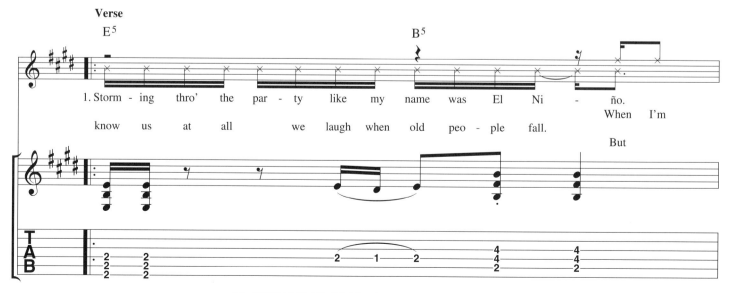

1. Storm-ing thro' the par-ty like my name was El Ni - ño.

know us at all we laugh when old peo-ple fall.

When I'm

But

14

15

19

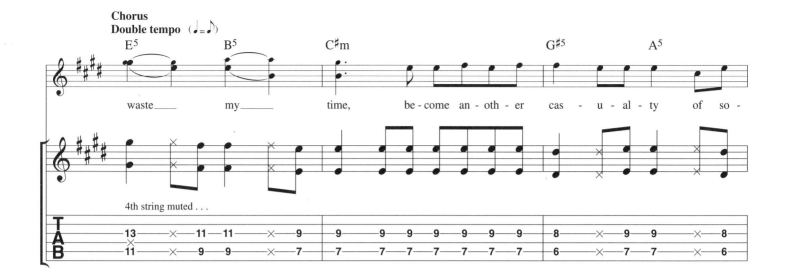

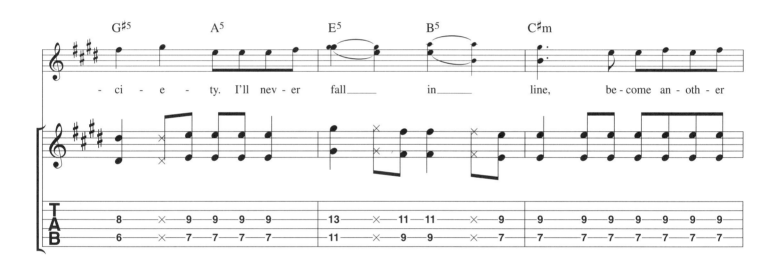

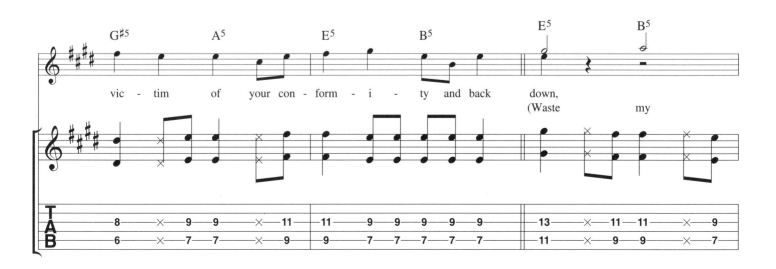

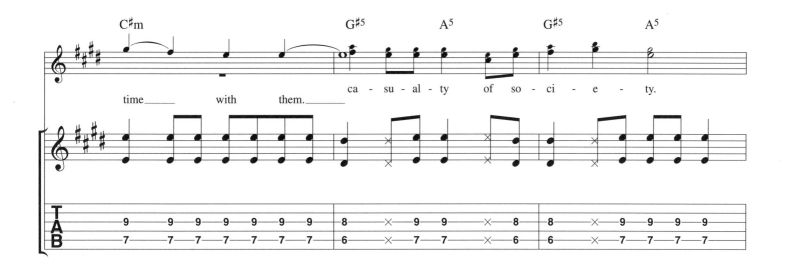

ca - su - al - ty of so - ci - e - ty.

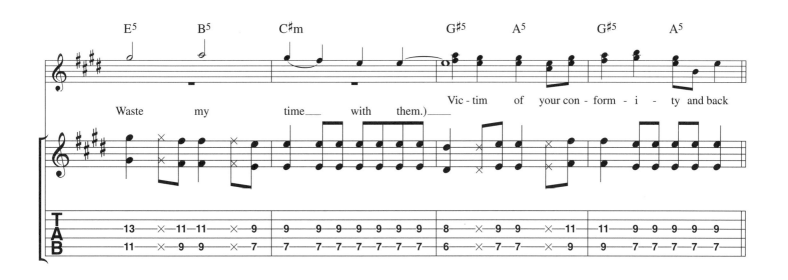

Waste my time____ with them.)____ Vic - tim of your con - form - i - ty and back

down.

* w/echo repeats

FLAVOR OF THE WEAK

Words & Music by Stacy Jones

Chorus

Her boy - friend, he don't_ know an - y - thing a - bout_ her. He's_ too_ stoned, Nin - ten - do. I wish_ that I could make_ her see._ She's just_ the fla - vor of_ the weak._

Her boy - friend, he don't_ know an - y - thing

27

28

HIGHLY EVOLVED

Words & Music by Craig Nicholls

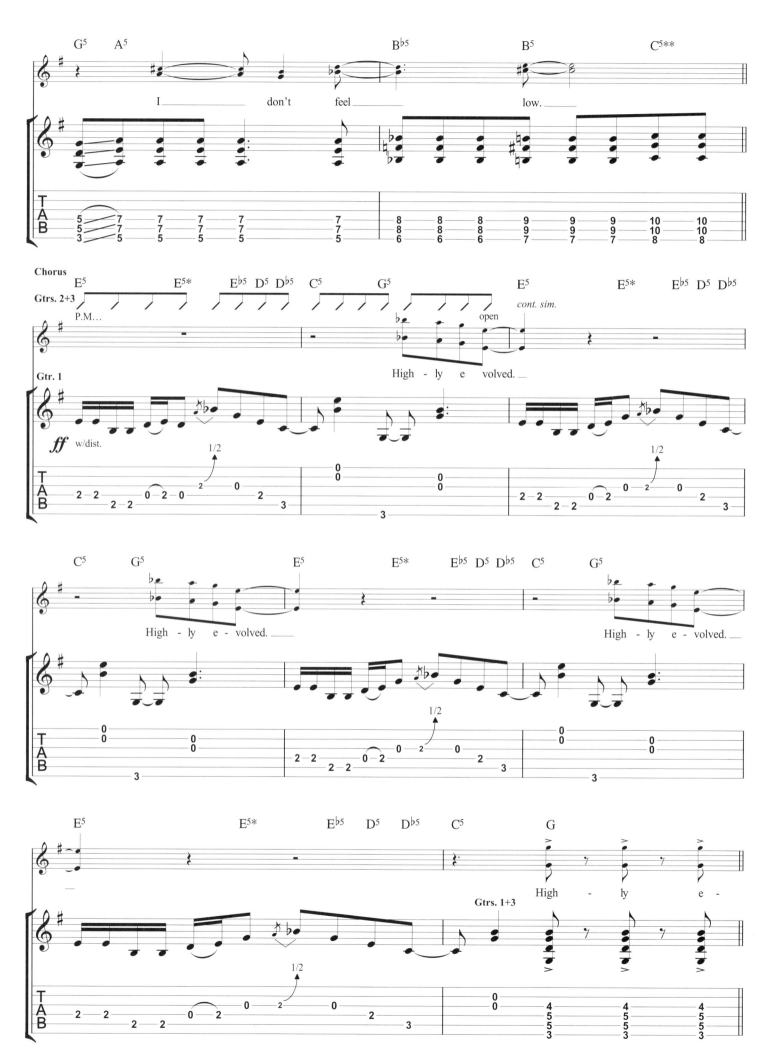

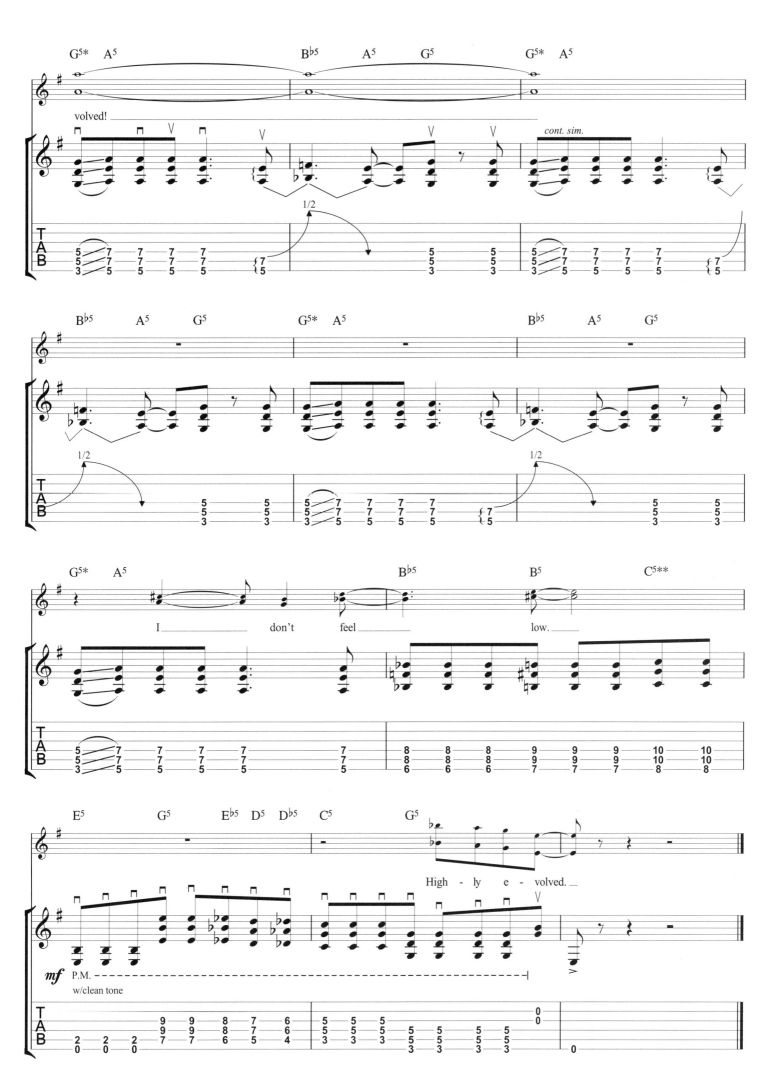

IN MY PLACE

Words & Music by Guy Berryman, Jon Buckland, Will Champion & Chris Martin

*Chord names represent actual sounding chords.
Chord shape represents chord with respect to capo.

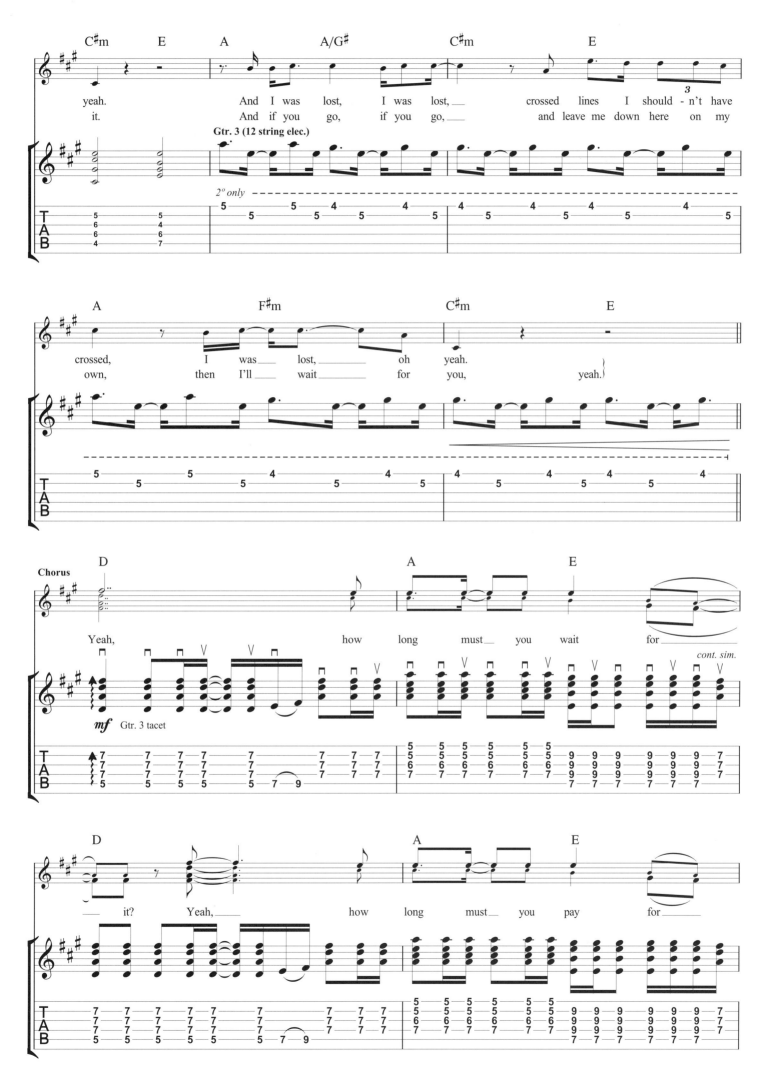

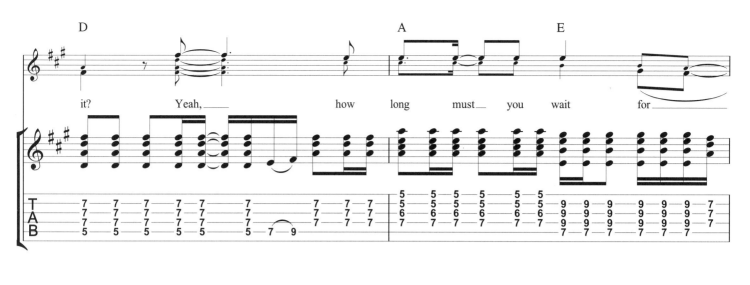

it? Yeah,_____ how long must___ you wait for_____

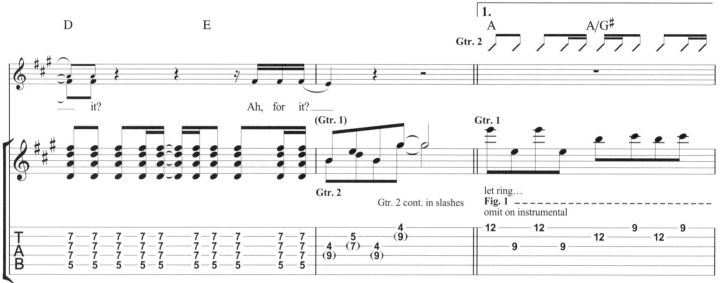

it? Ah, for it?_____

Gtr. 2 cont. in slashes

let ring…
Fig. 1 —
omit on instrumental

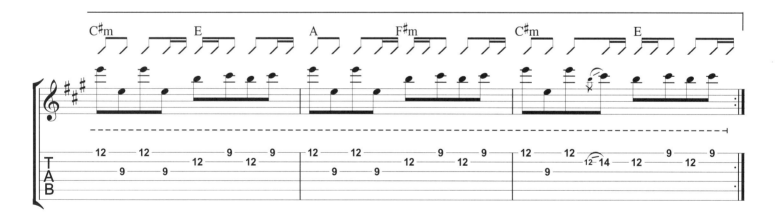

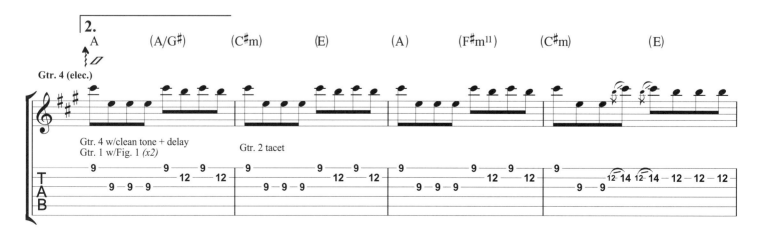

Gtr. 4 w/clean tone + delay
Gtr. 1 w/Fig. 1 *(x2)*

Gtr. 2 tacet

IN YOUR WORLD

Lyrics & Music by Matthew Bellamy

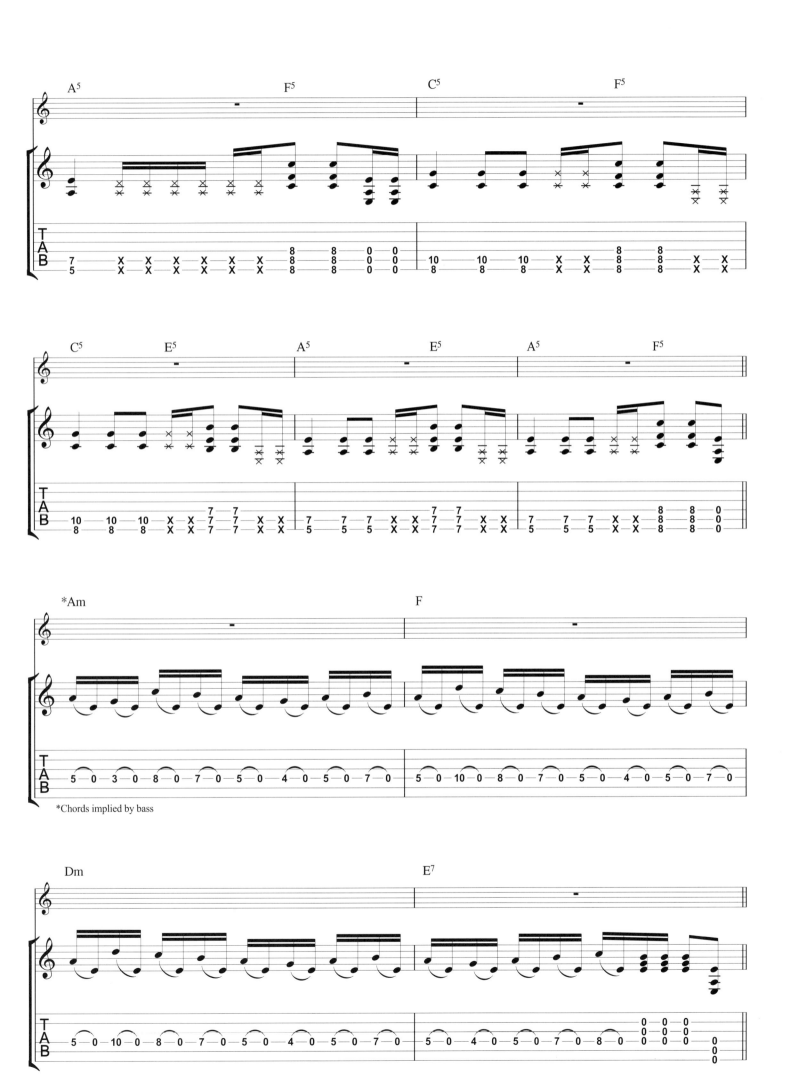

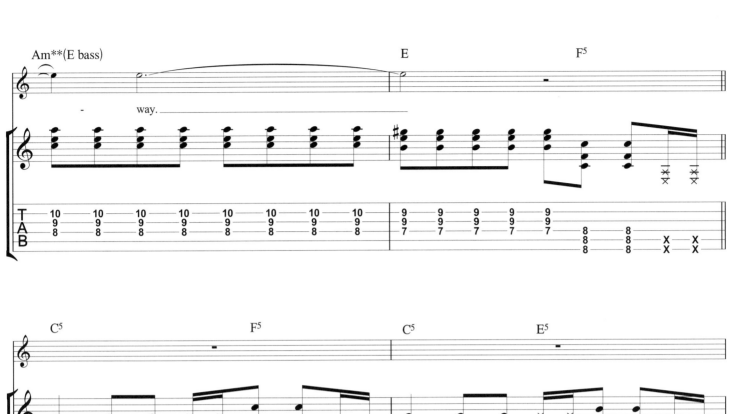

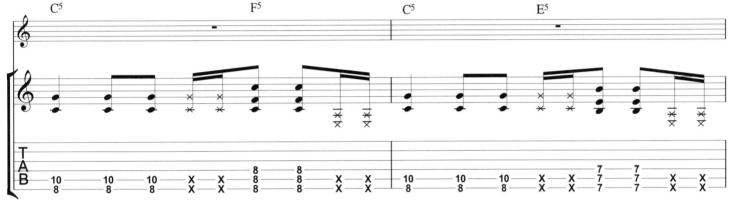

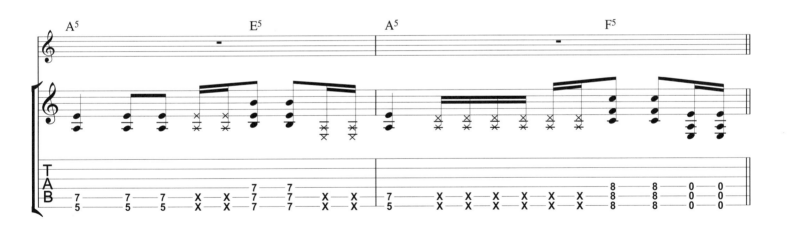

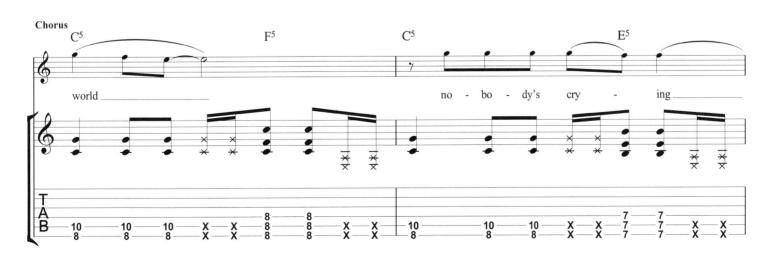

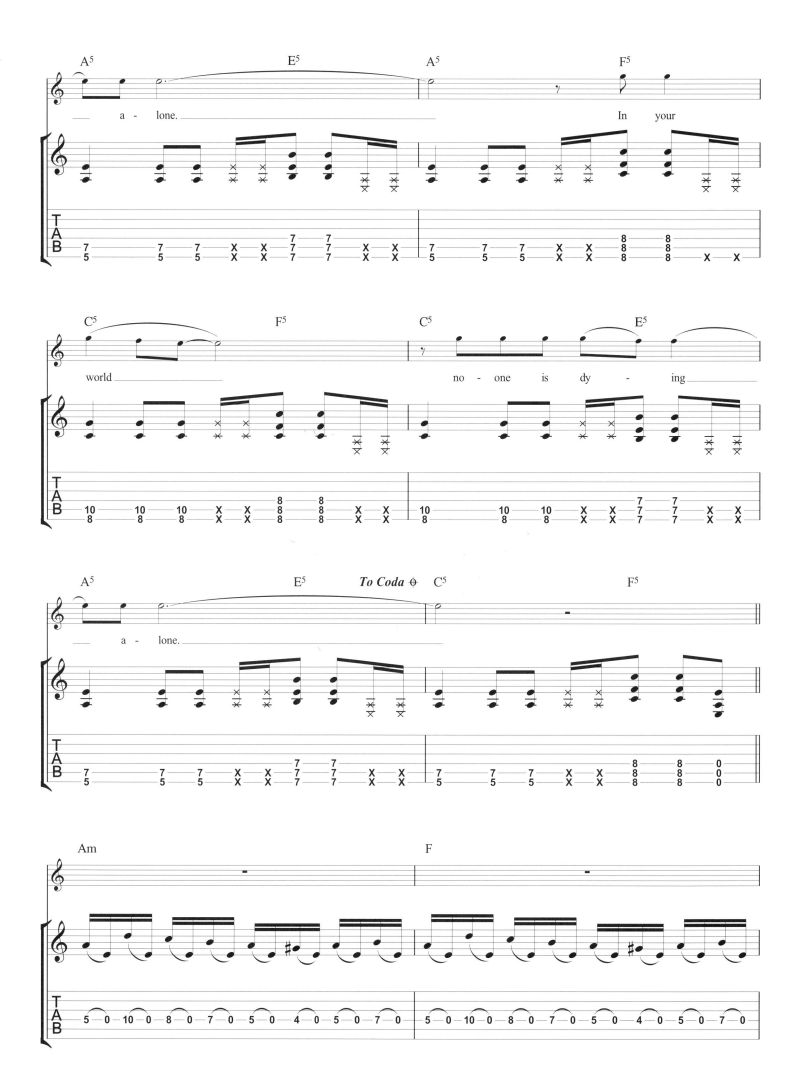

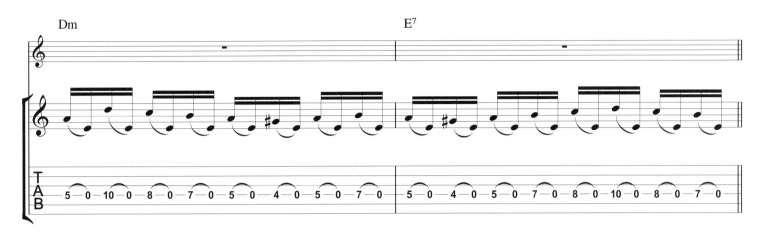

Verse

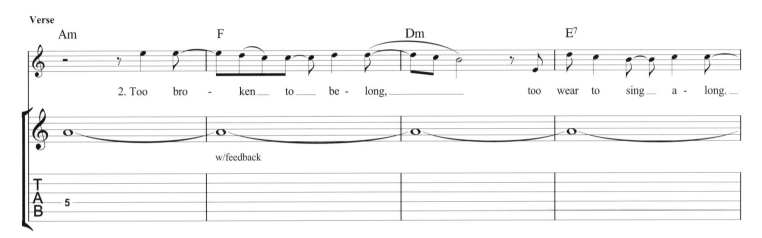

2. Too bro - ken to be - long, _____ too wear to sing a - long. _____

w/feedback

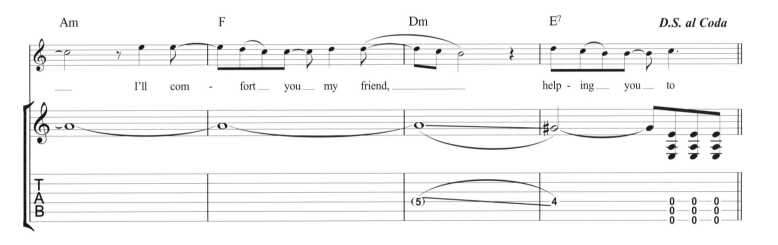

_____ I'll com - fort you my friend, _____ help - ing _ you _ to

D.S. al Coda

Coda

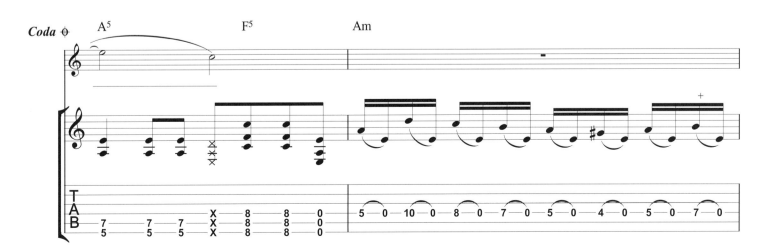

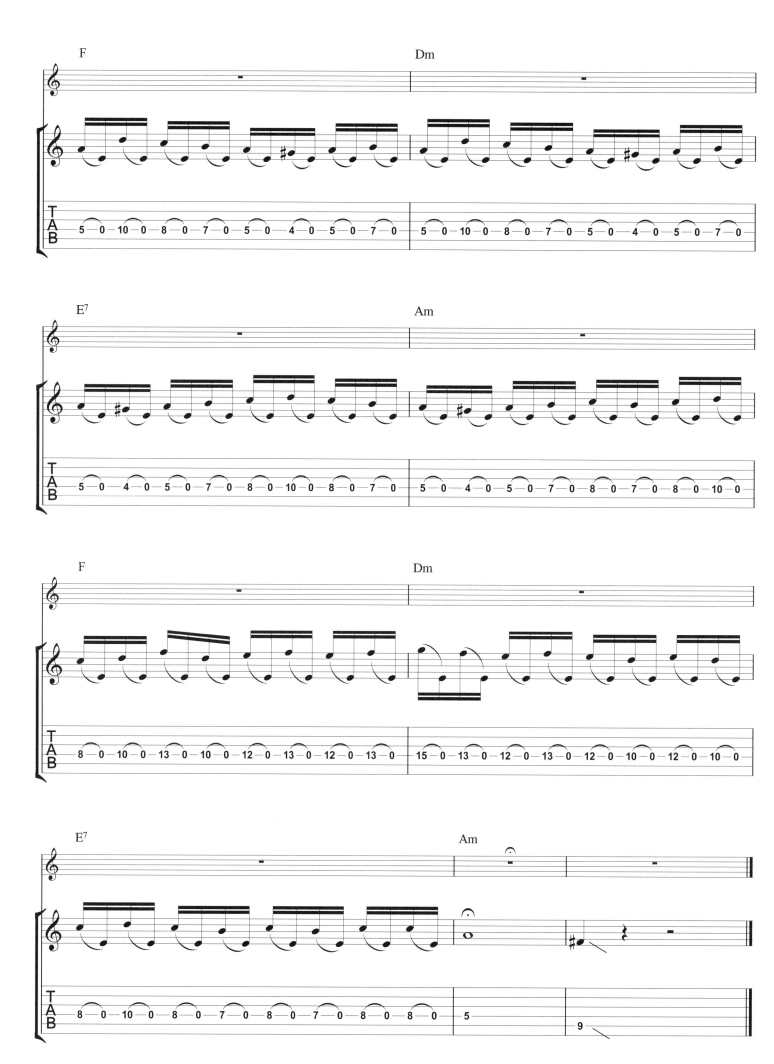

JUST A DAY

Words & Music by Grant Nicholas

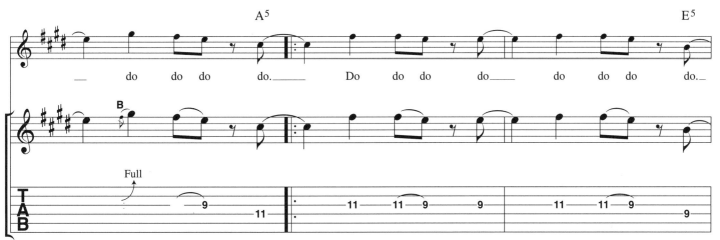

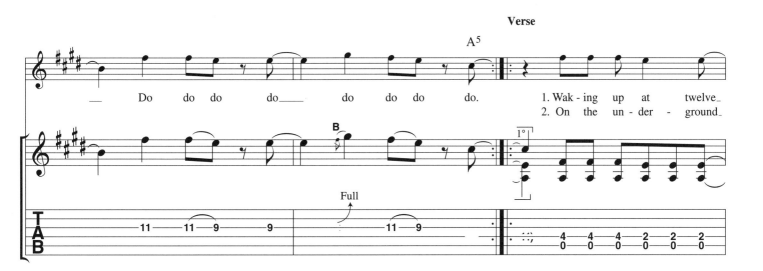

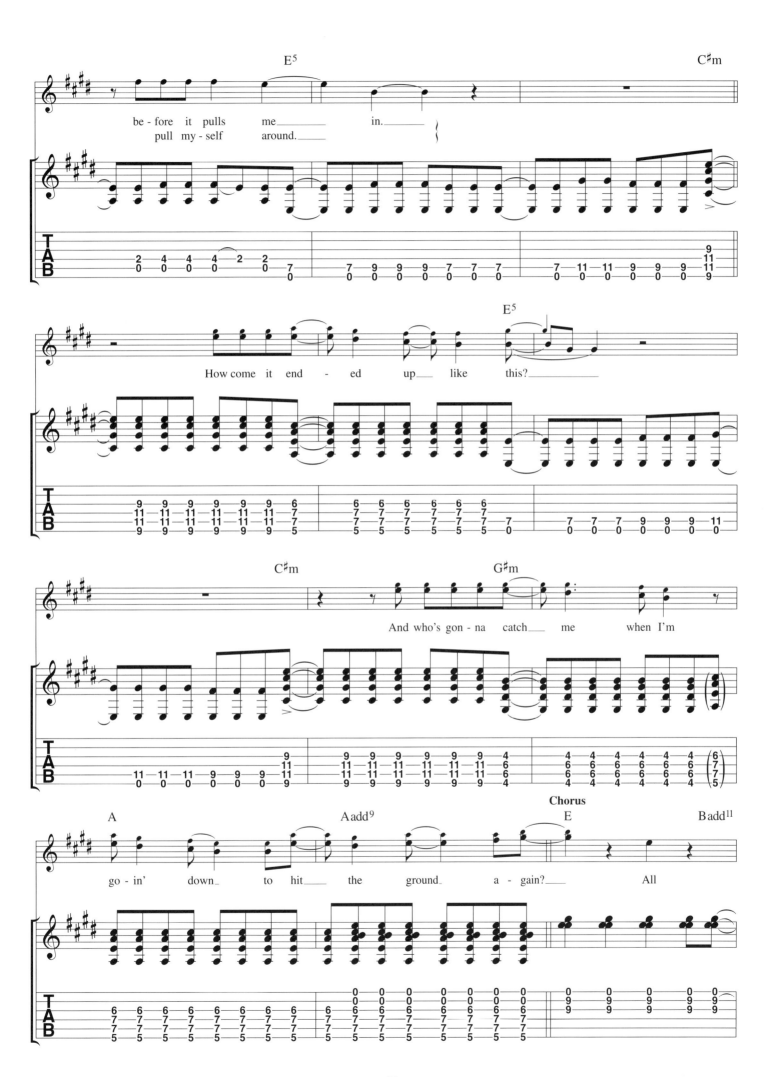

MOVIES

Words & Music by Dryden Mitchell, Terence Corso, Tye Zamora & Mike Cosgrove

Intro

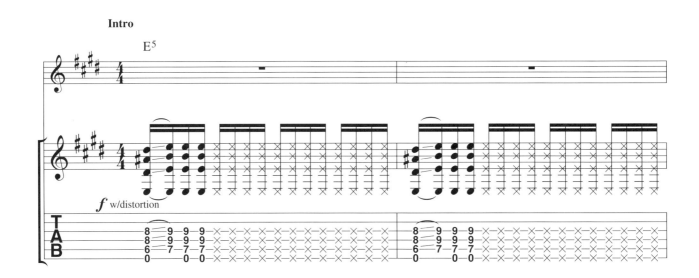

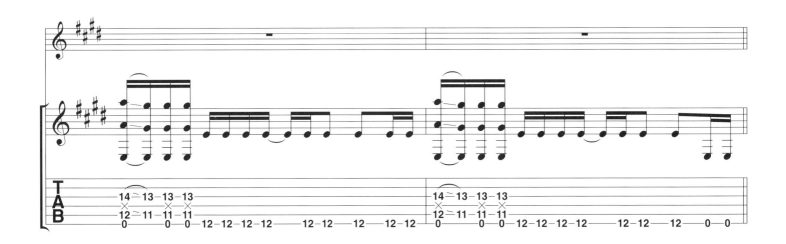

Verse

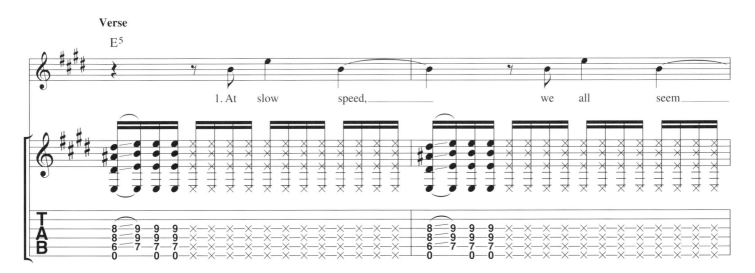

1. At slow speed,_____ we all seem_____

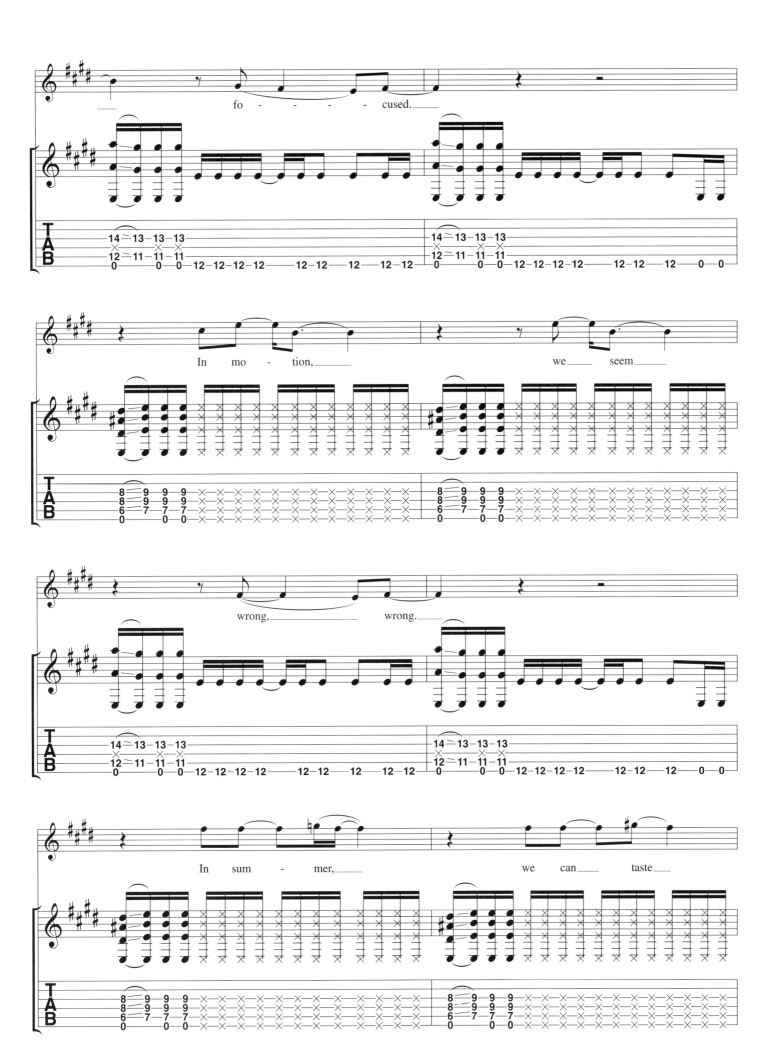

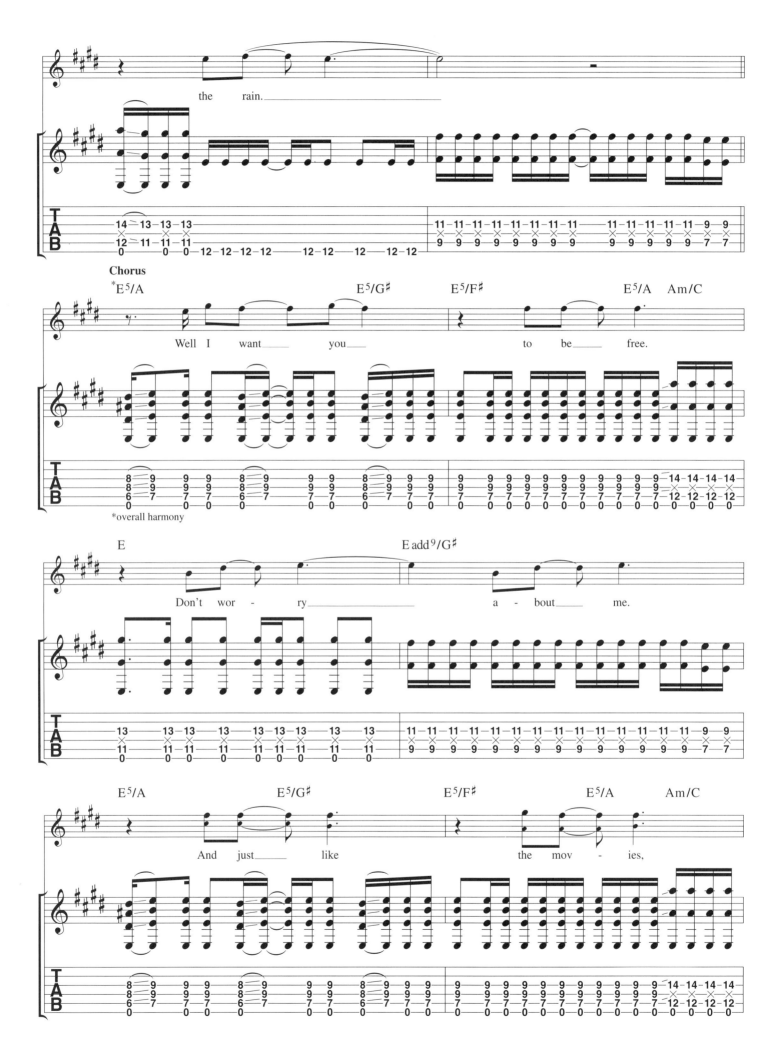

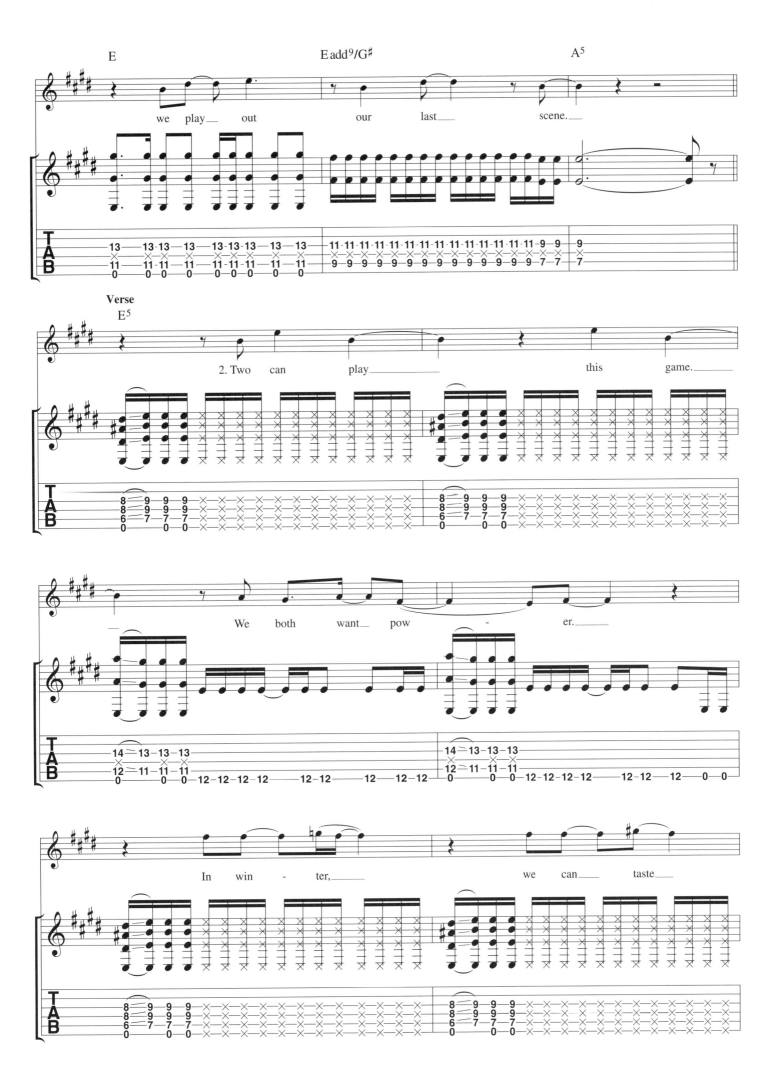

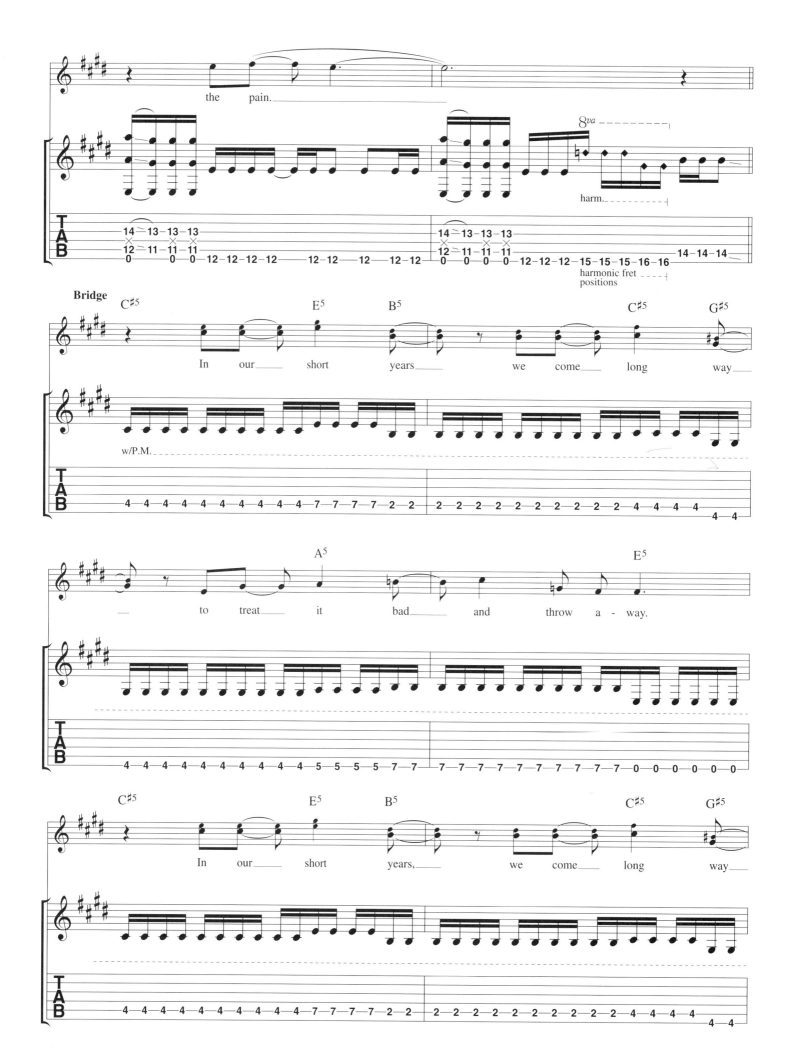

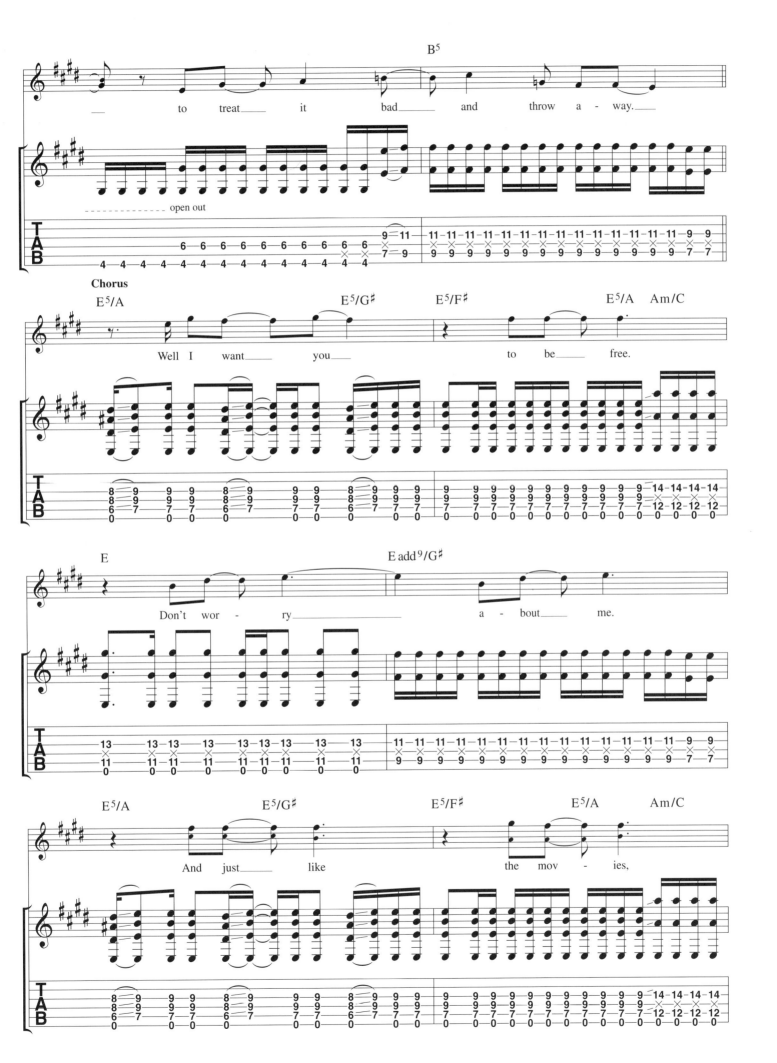

59

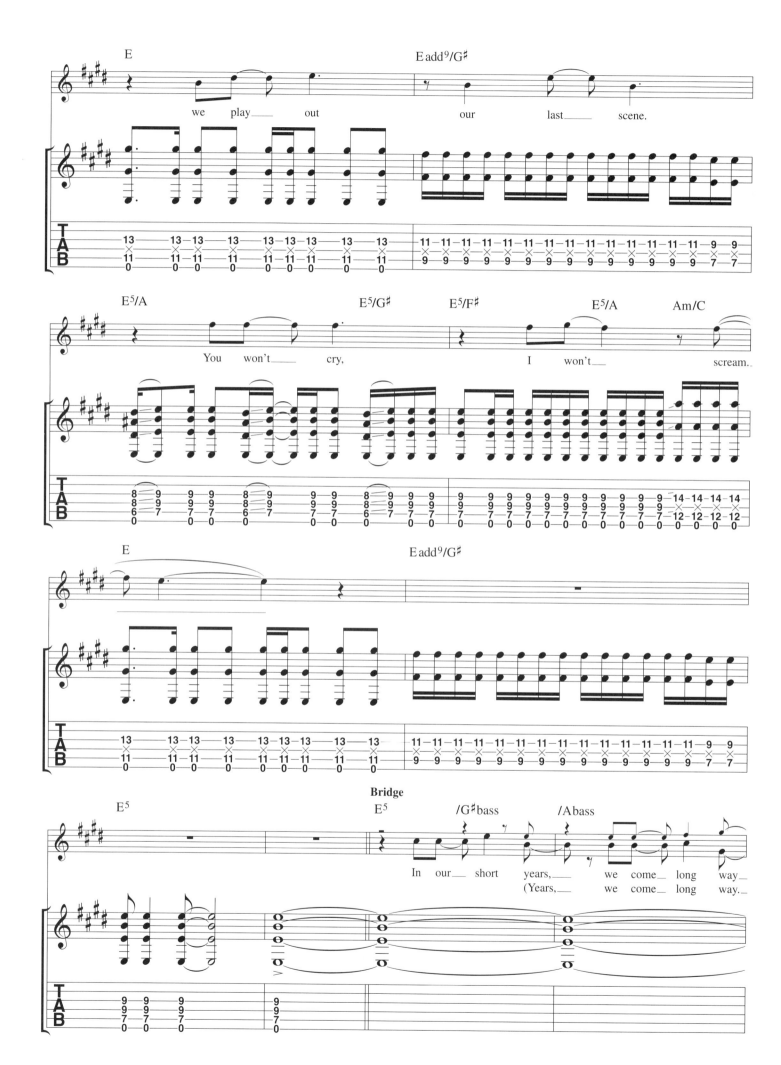

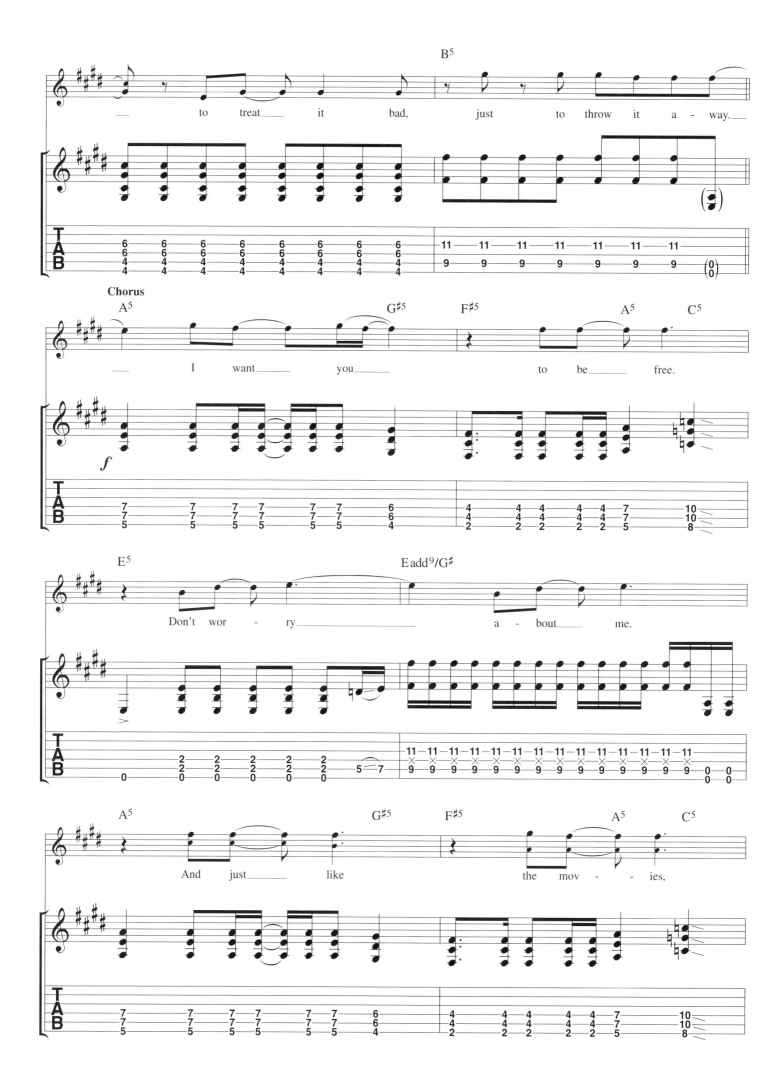

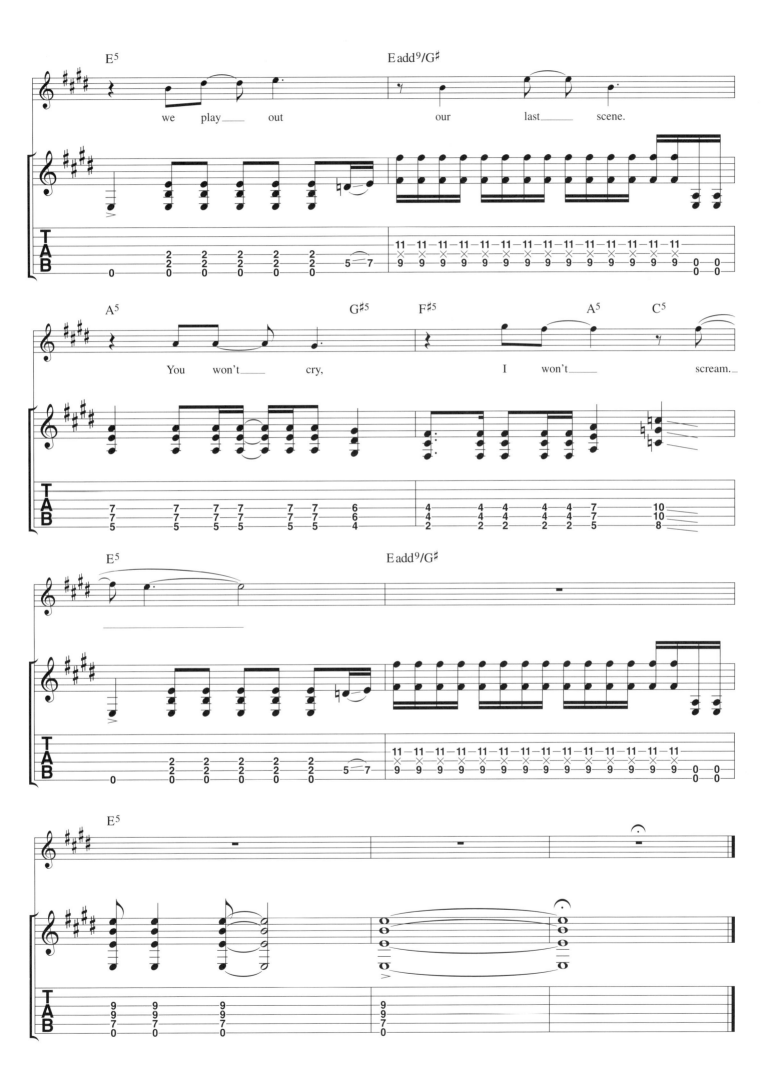

POINTS OF AUTHORITY

Words & Music by Chester Bennington, Rob Bourdon, Brad Delson, Joseph Hahn & Mike Shinoda

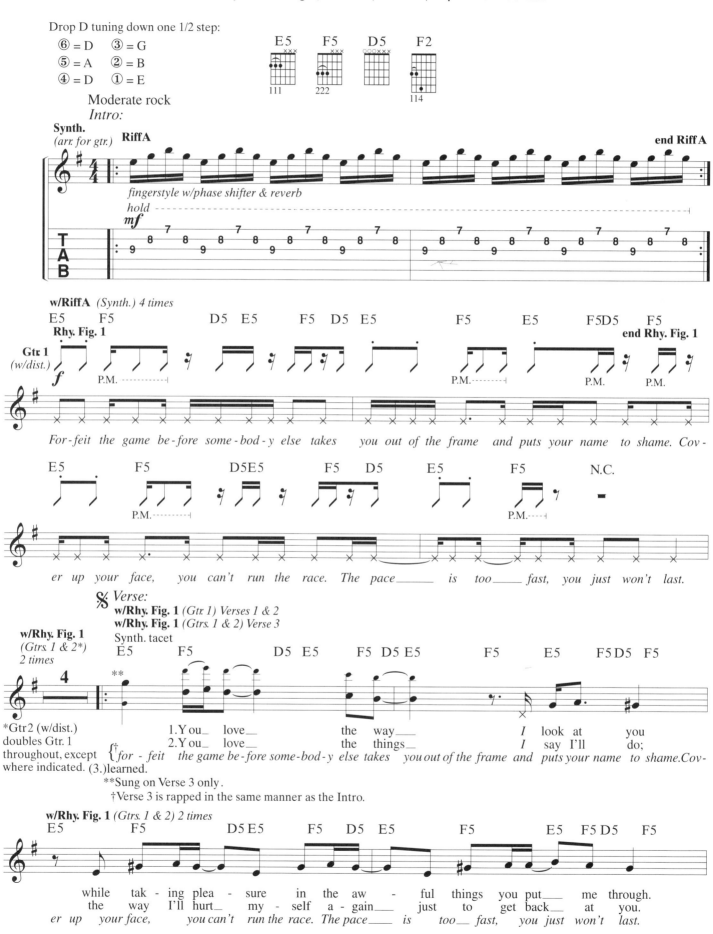

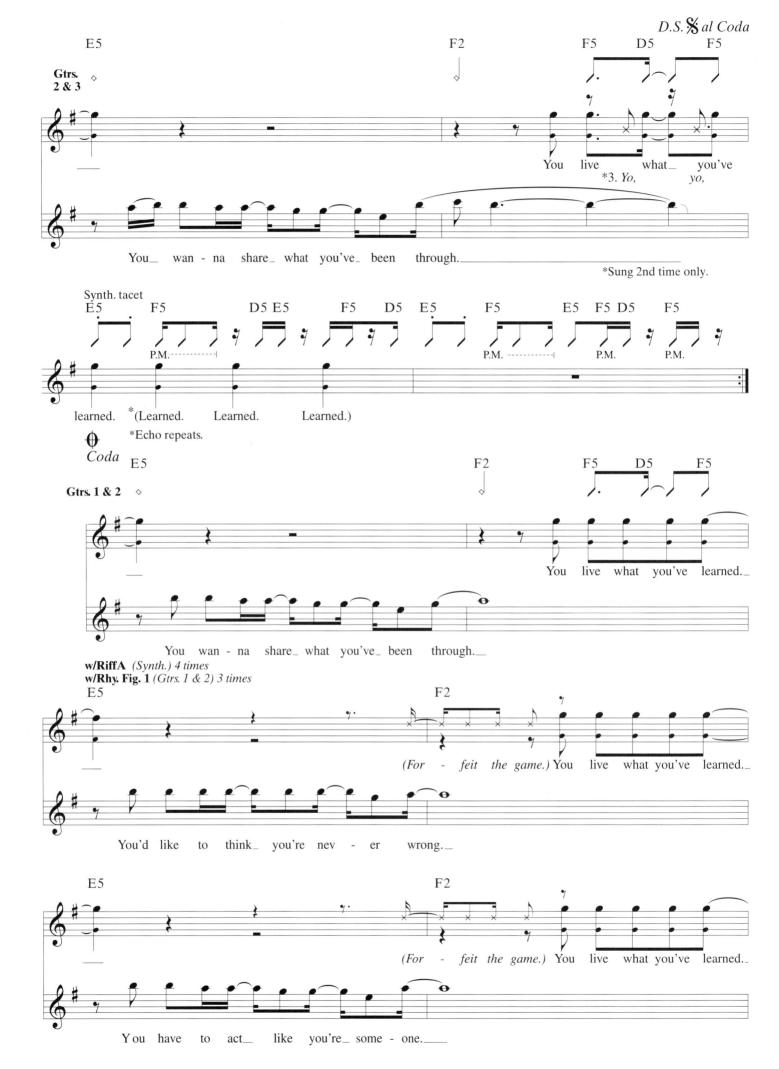

E5   F2

(For - feit the game.) You live what you've learned.___

You want some - one___ to hurt___ like you.___

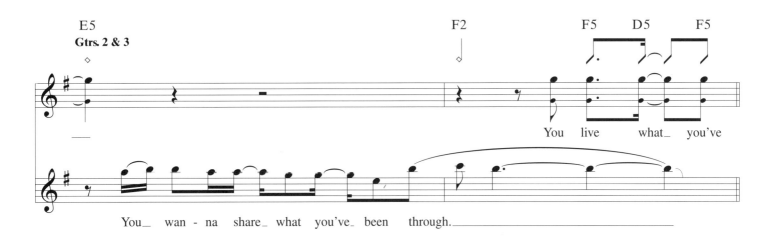

E5   F2   F5   D5   F5

Gtrs. 2 & 3

You live what___ you've

You___ wan - na share___ what you've___ been through.___

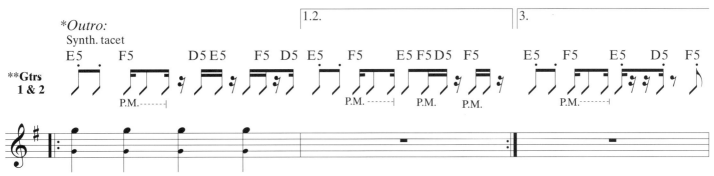

Outro:
Synth. tacet

**Gtrs
1 & 2

E5   F5   D5 E5   F5 D5 E5   F5   E5 F5 D5 F5   E5   F5   E5   D5   F5

P.M.------| P.M.------| P.M.   P.M.   P.M.------|

|1. 2. |3.

learned. (Learned. Learned.   Learned.)
(Sing 1st time only.)

*This section, as heard on the recording, was edited using Pro Tools.
Therefore, the transcription has been arranged so as to emulate the effect on the recording as closely as possible.
**Doubled by ad lib. scat-style vocal.

Echo repeats.

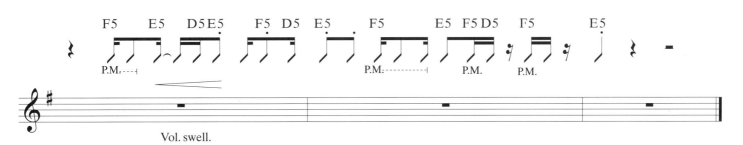

F5   E5   D5 E5   F5 D5 E5   F5   E5 F5 D5 F5   E5

P.M.----| P.M.------| P.M.   P.M.

Vol. swell.

LITTLE BY LITTLE

Words & Music by Noel Gallagher

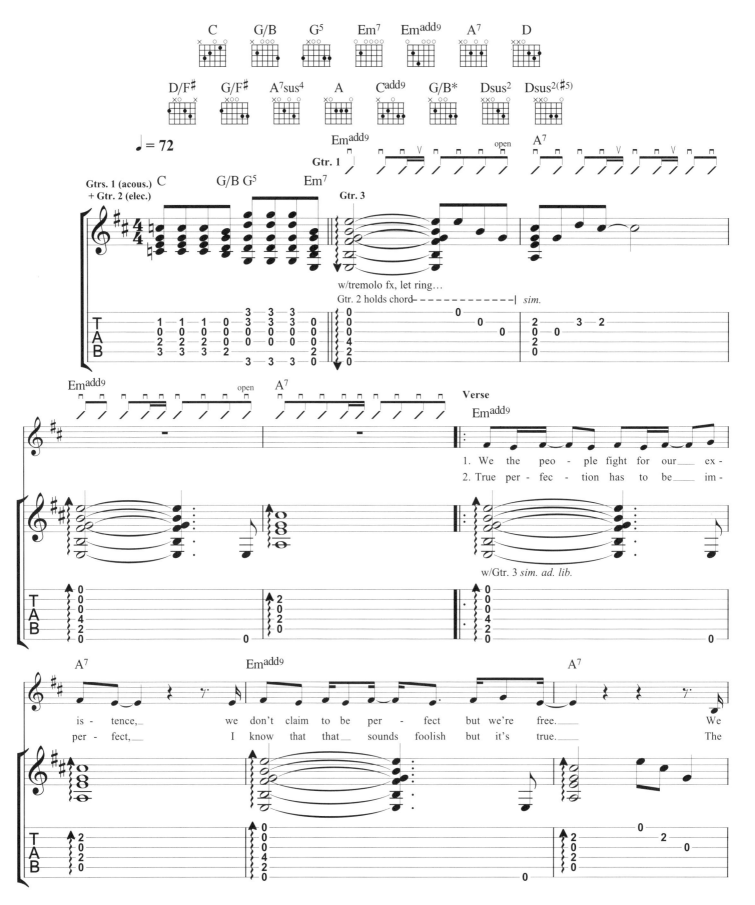

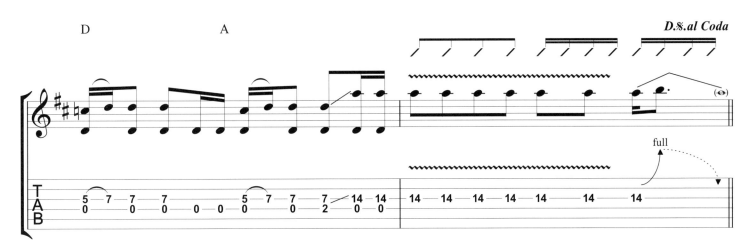

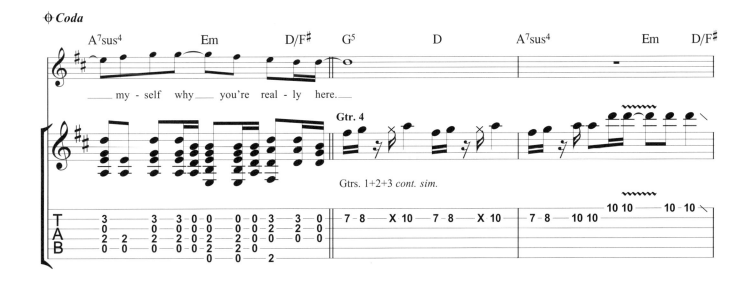

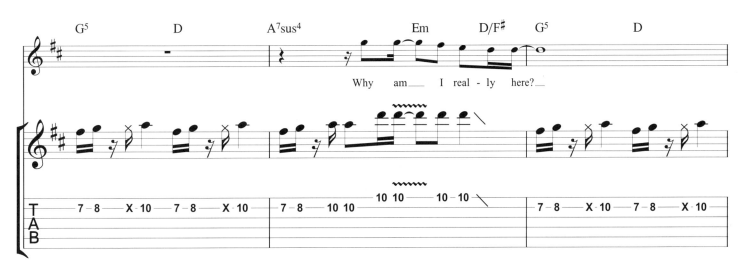

Why am___ I real - ly here?___

SOMETIMES

Words & Music by Tim Wheeler

*Symbols in parentheses represent chord names with respect to capoed guitar (TAB 0 = 7th fret).
Symbols above represent actual sounding chords.

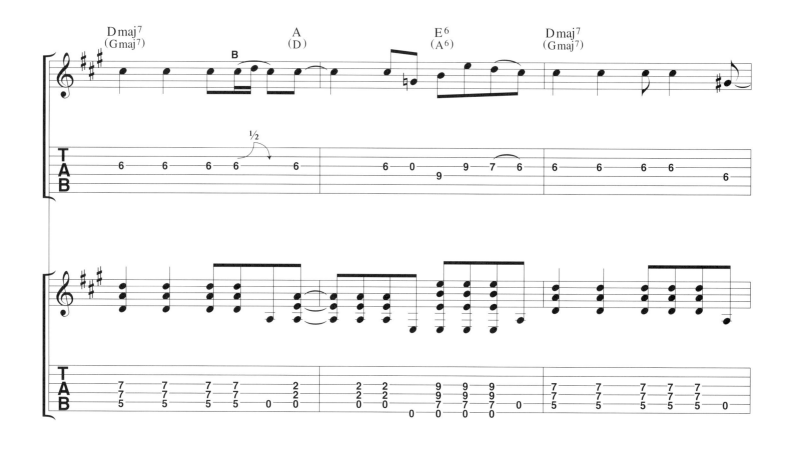

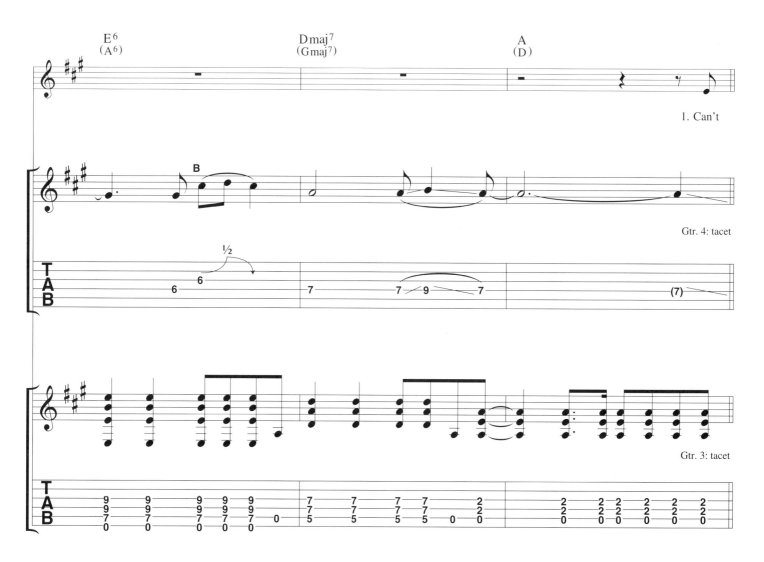

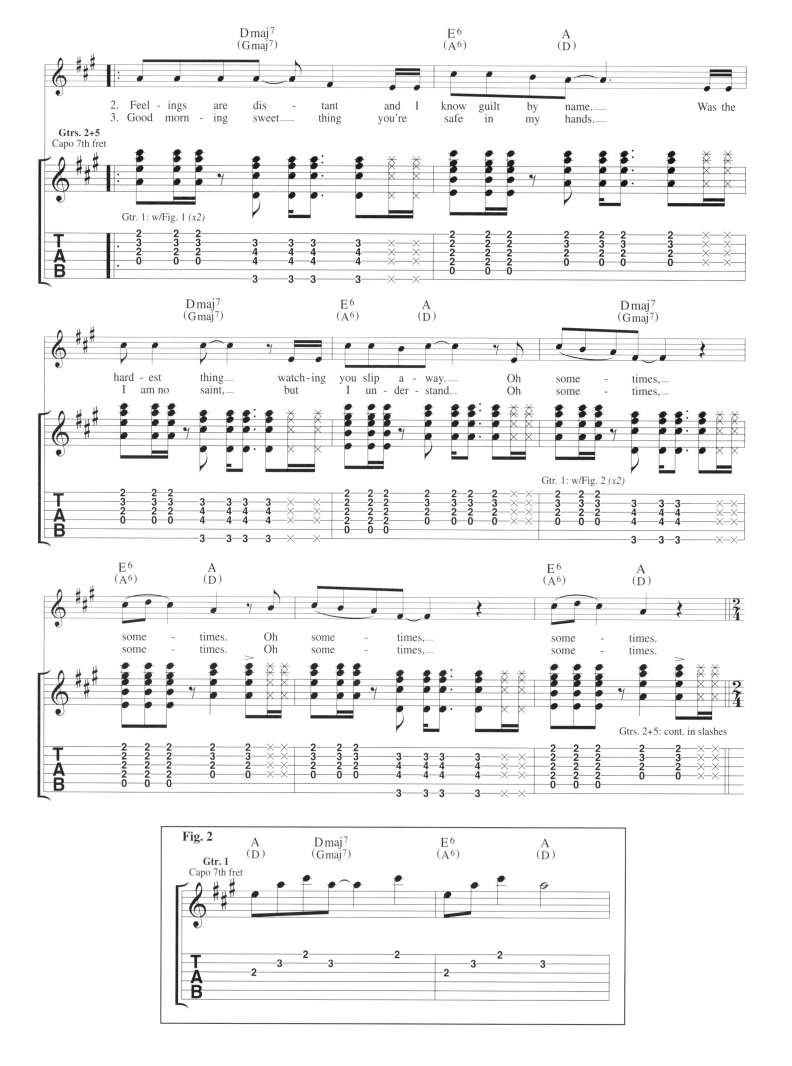

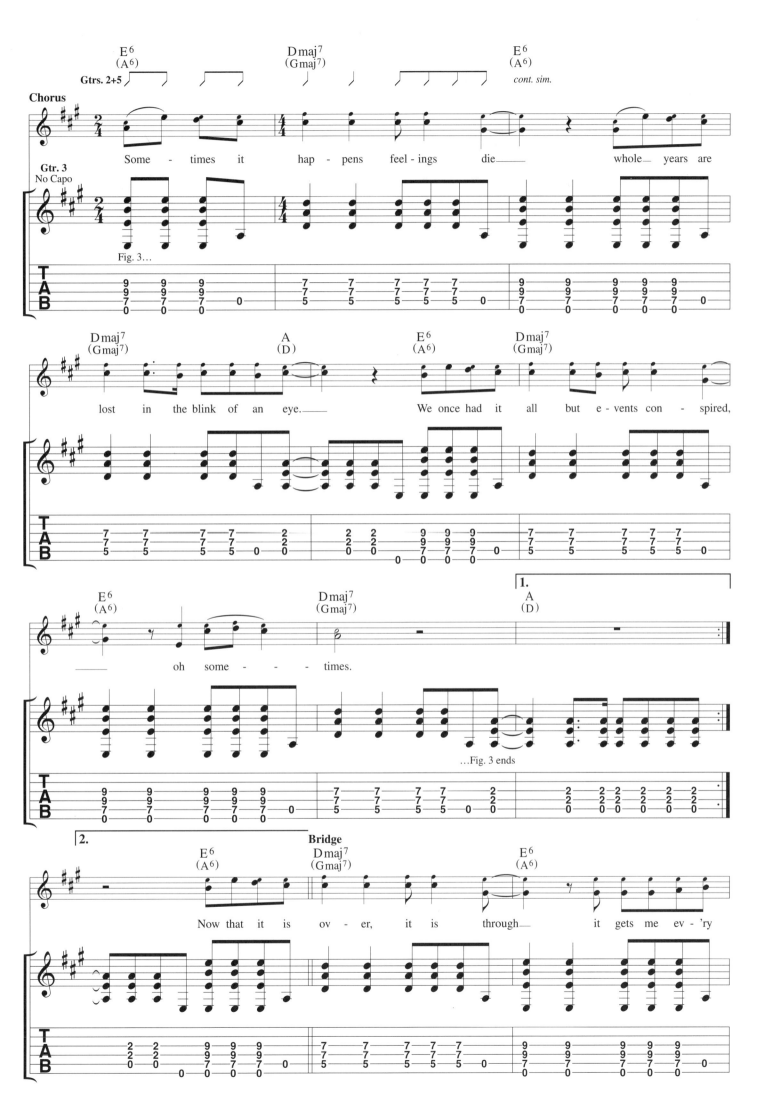

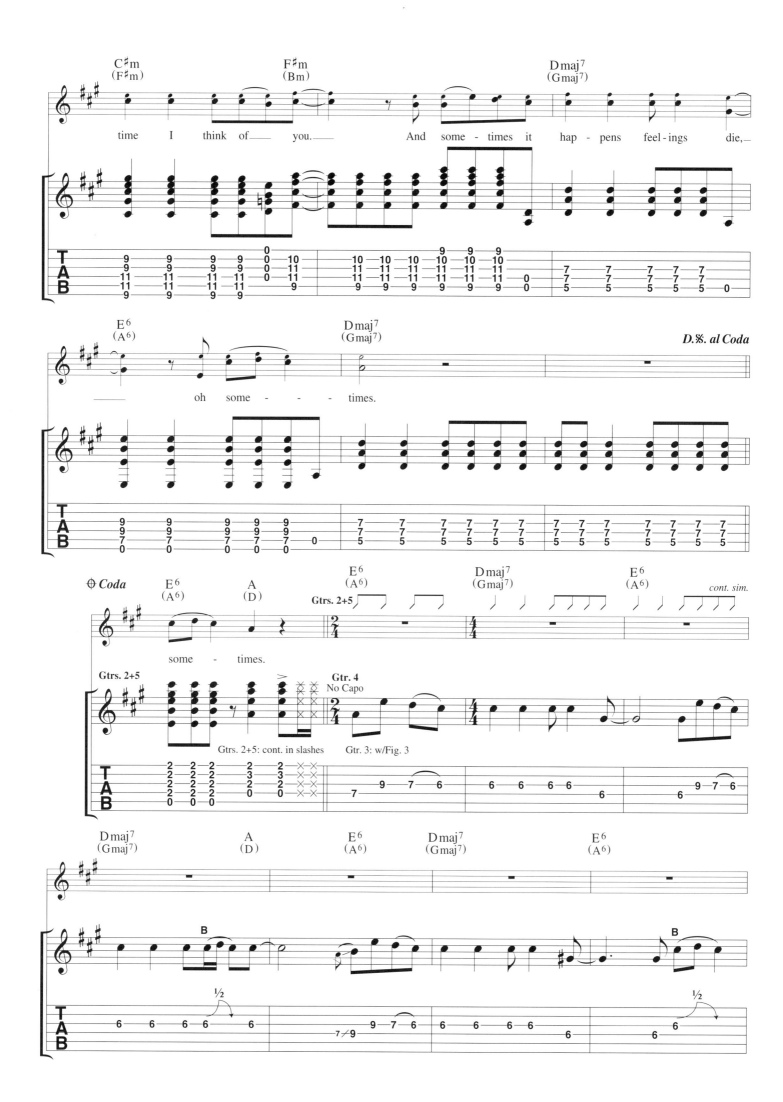

78

SIDE

Words & Music by Fran Healy

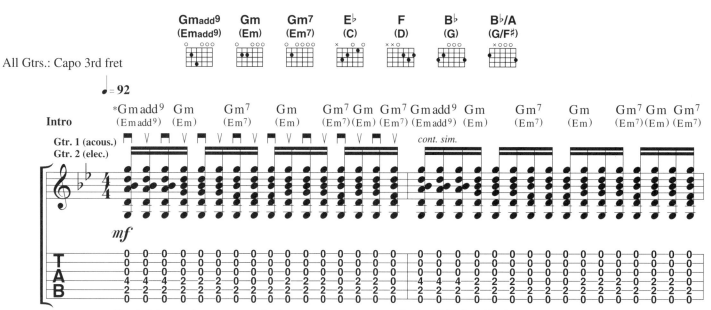

All Gtrs.: Capo 3rd fret

*Symbols in parentheses represent chord names with respect to capoed guitar (TAB 0= 3rd fret).
 Symbols above represent actual sounding chords.

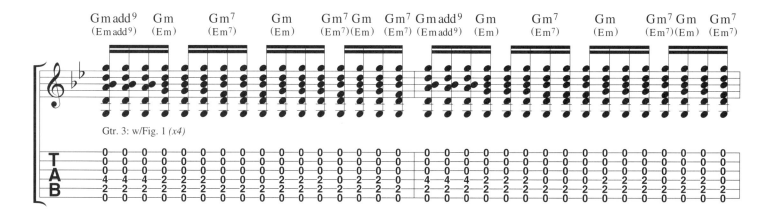

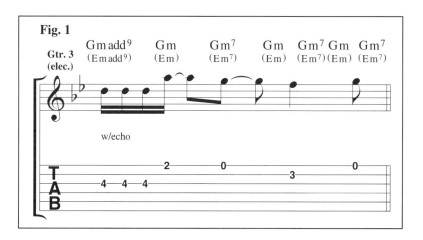

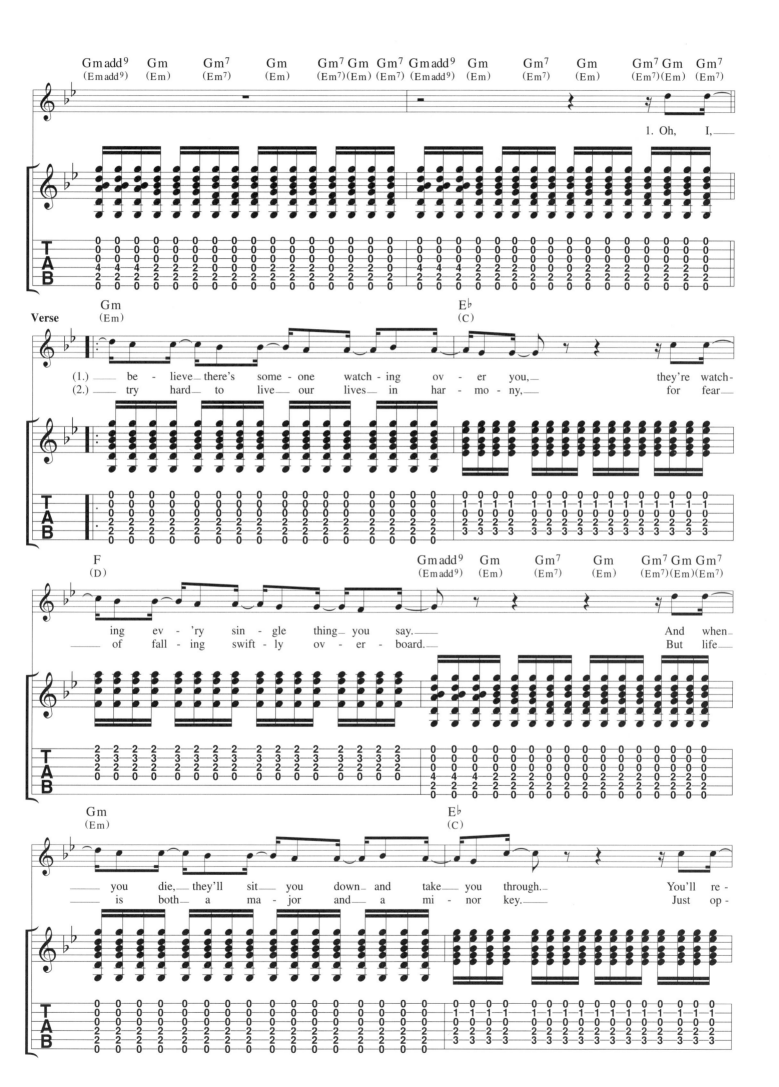

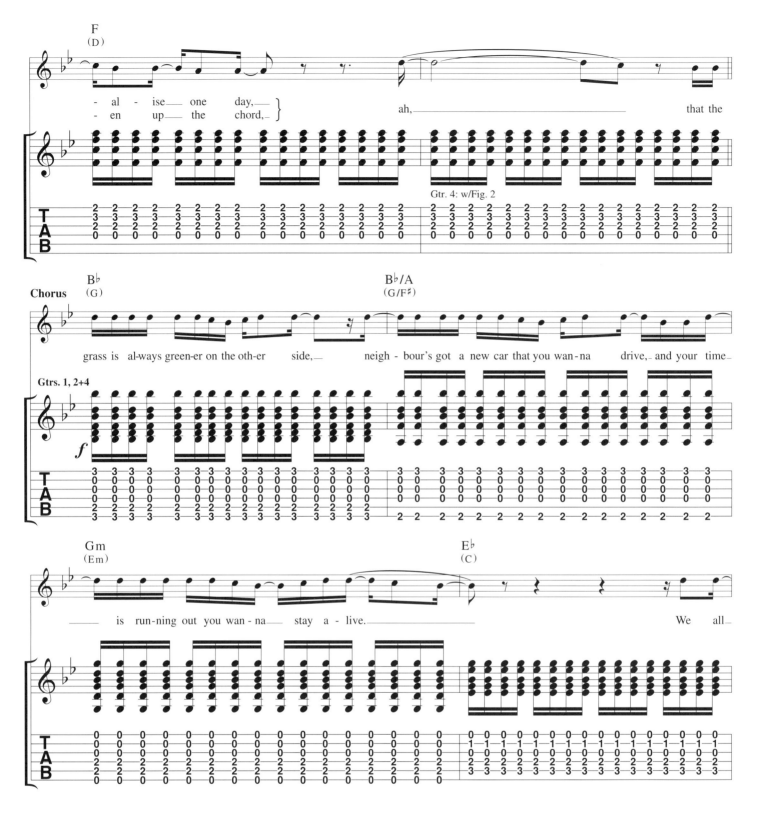

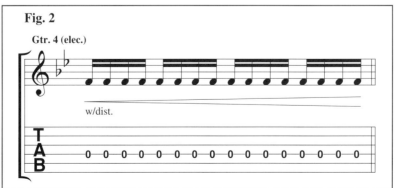

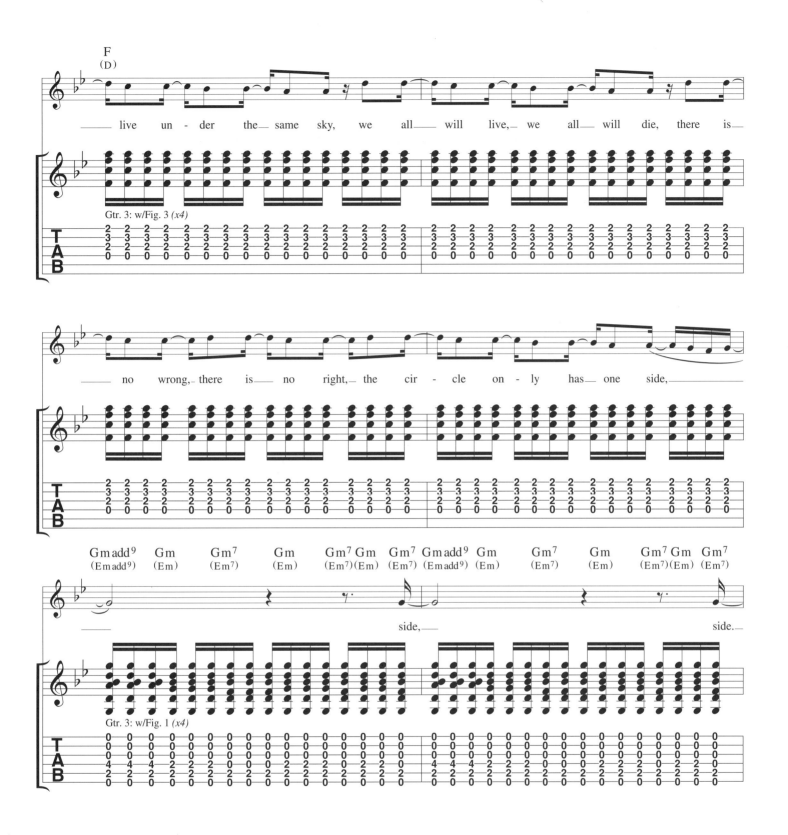

live un-der the same sky, we all will live, we all will die, there is

no wrong, there is no right, the cir-cle on-ly has one side,

side, side.

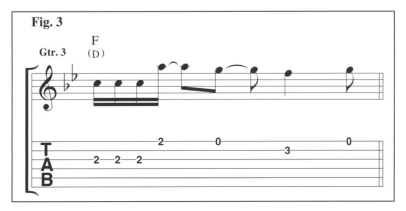

Fig. 3

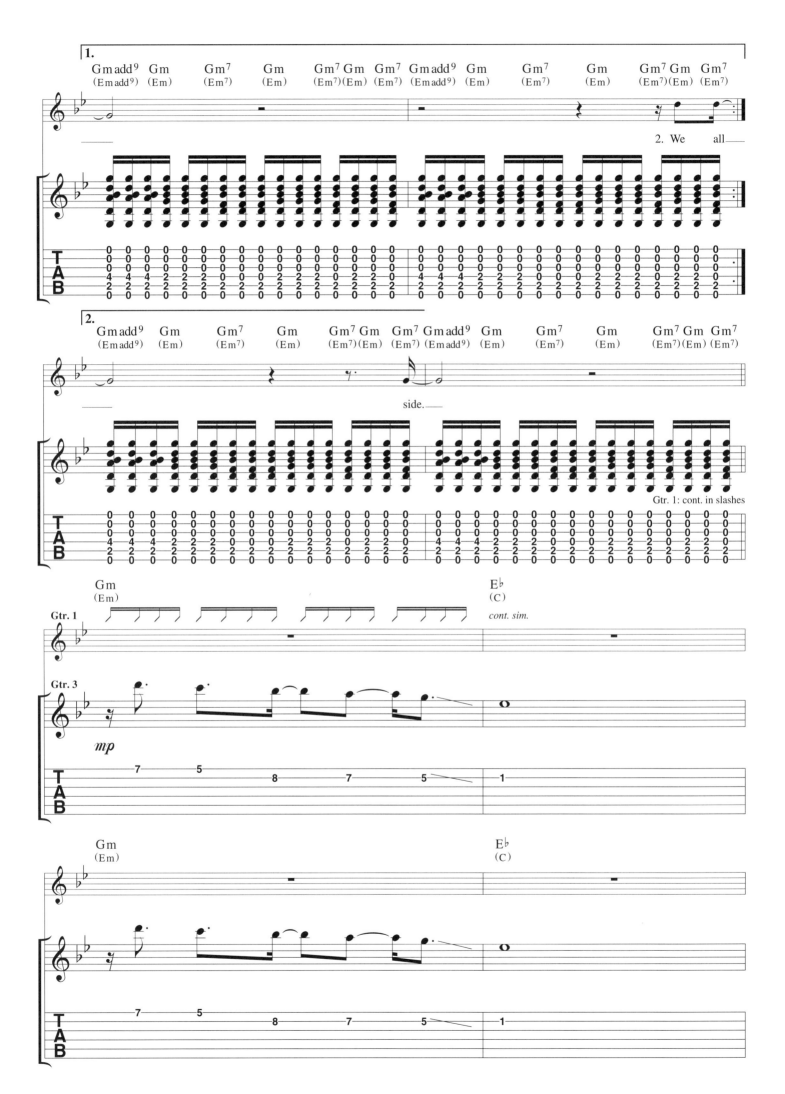

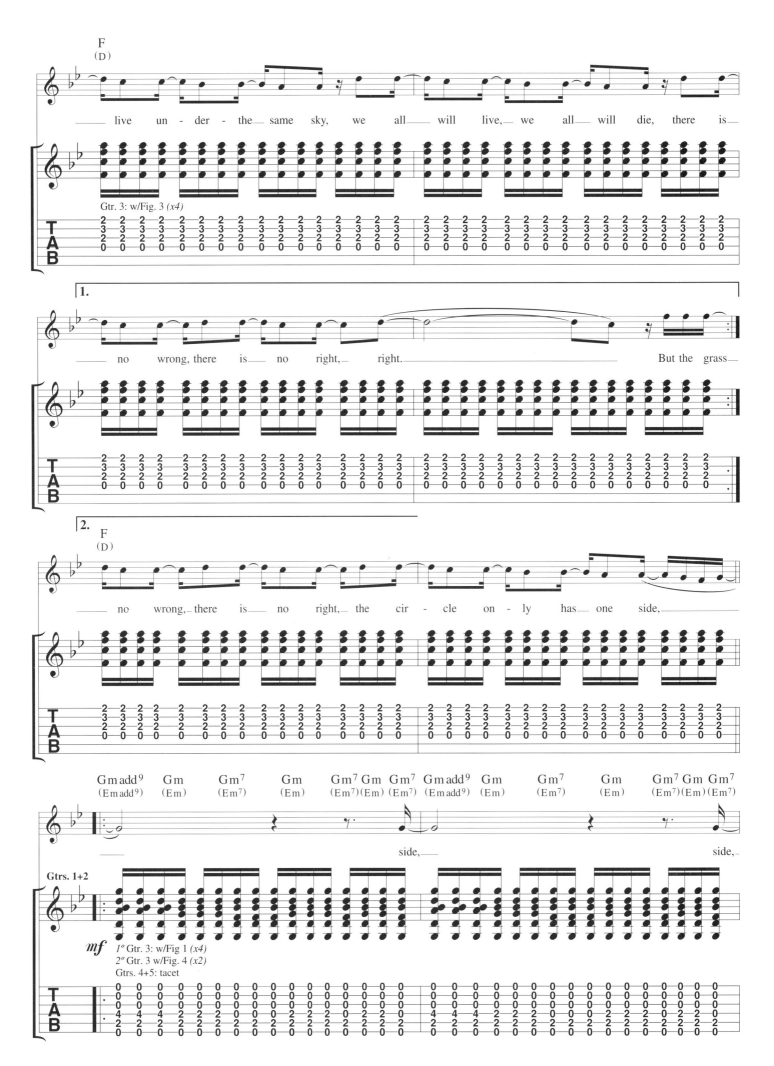

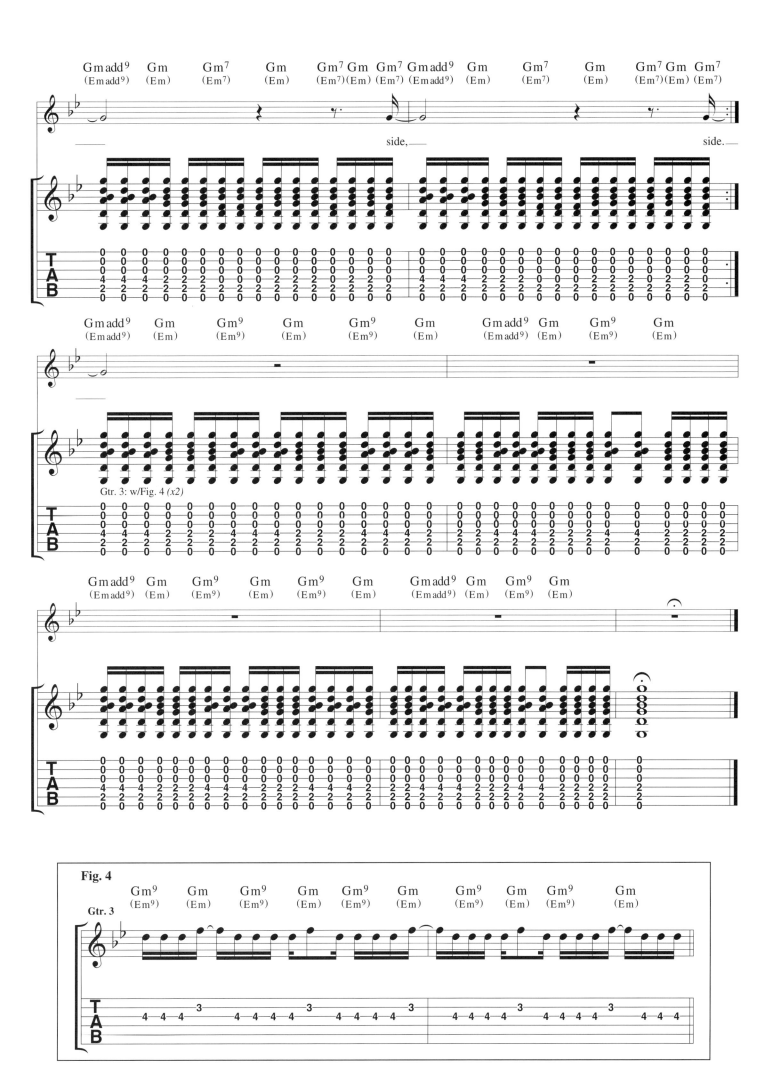

VEGAS TWO TIMES

Words & Music by Kelly Jones

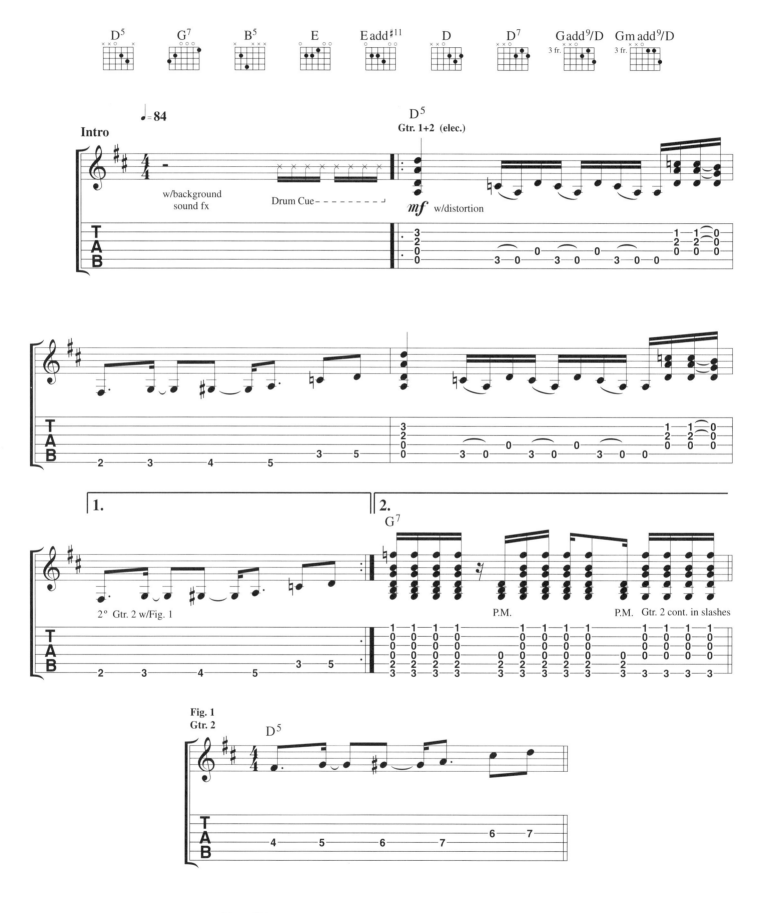

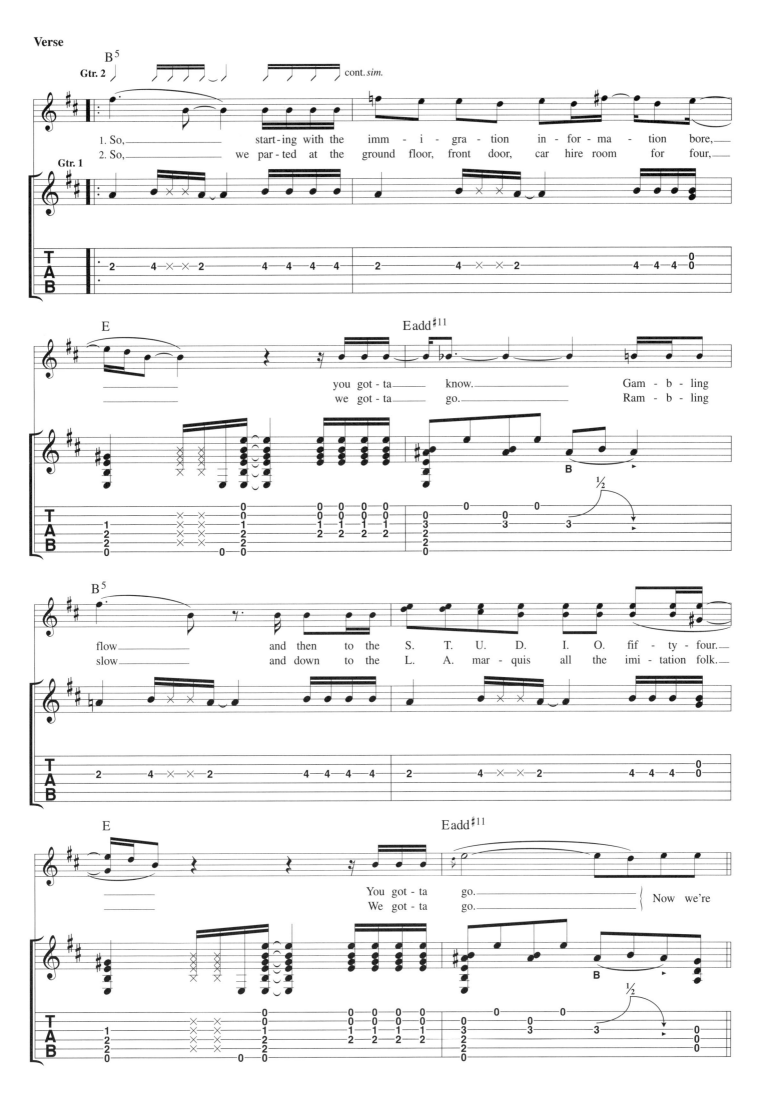

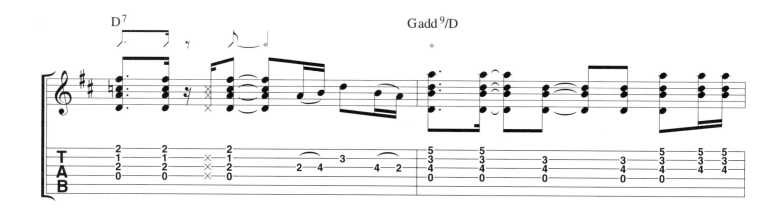

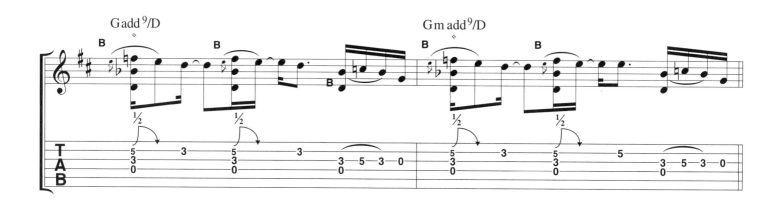

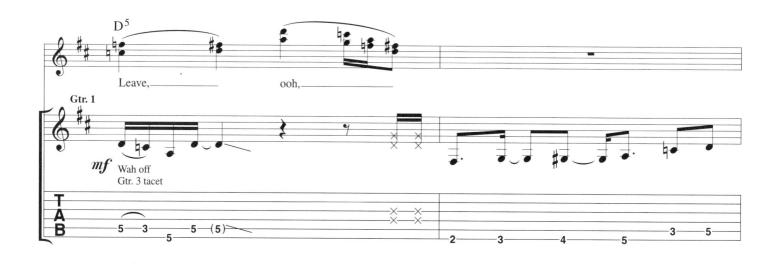

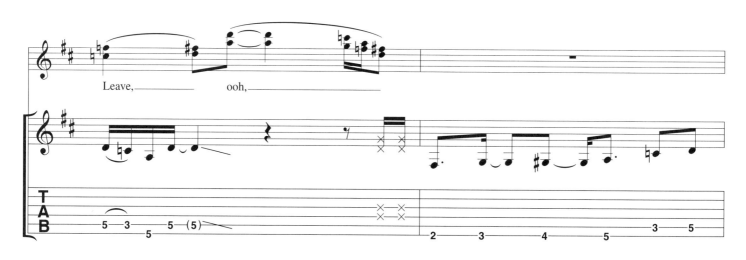

D.%. al Coda

Leave, _____ ooh, _____

Leave, _____ ooh, _____ And now we've

Gtr. 2 w/Fig. 3

w/wah - - - - - - - - - - - - - - -

⊕ *Coda*

D5

come a - gain___ we'll make you fly._____

Gtrs. 1+2

Fig. 3
Gtr. 2   D5

w/feedback - - - - - - - - - - - - - - -   P.H.   Full

B

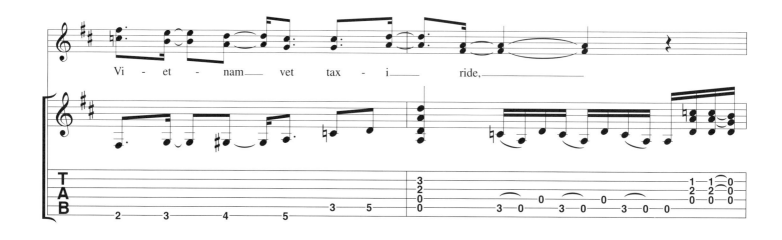

Vi - et - nam — vet tax - i — ride,

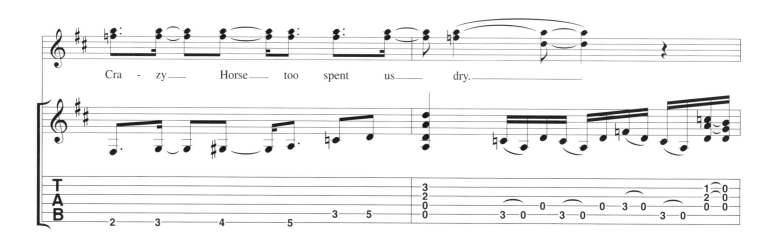

Cra - zy — Horse — too spent us — dry.

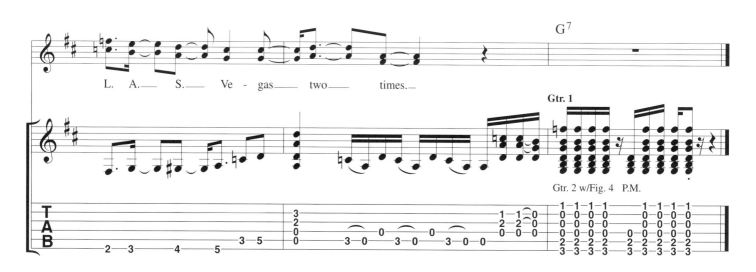

L. A. — S. — Ve - gas — two — times.

G⁷

Gtr. 1

Gtr. 2 w/Fig. 4 P.M.

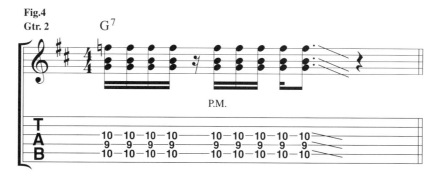

Fig.4
Gtr. 2   G⁷

P.M.